GLASS WC

Tom Gillespie is a Scottish-born novel and short story writer, now living in exile in Bath, England. His stories have been published worldwide in journals, e-zines and creative anthologies. His latest novel, *The Strange Book of Jacob Boyce* (Vine Leaves Press), has been praised by critics as 'brilliantly unsettling' and 'obsessively compelling'. Tom is a graduate of Glasgow University and works as an English lecturer. For more information, visit tom-gillespie.com.

Paul Cowan grew up in Falkirk in central Scotland. After leaving school, he trained as a welder, which took him up and down the country and abroad. He even dipped his toes in the North Sea and worked offshore. He has been honing his skill as a writer, using his own life experiences as his guide, for nearly twenty years. His short stories and poems have appeared in numerous magazines and anthologies. Paul can still be found in Falkirk and has a five-year-old daughter.

John McKenzie grew up in Menstrie, a small village in Scotland. He worked in the financial sector until returning to education in his mid-thirties. Six years and one undergraduate degree course later, John is about to complete his Master of Letters in Creative Writing from the University of Stirling. He is also working on his first novel.

Glass
Work
Humans

PAUL COWAN
TOM GILLESPIE
JOHN McKENZIE

Valley Press

First published in 2020 by Valley Press
Woodend, The Crescent, Scarborough, YO11 2PW
www.valleypressuk.com

First edition, first printing (October 2020)

ISBN 978-1-912436-38-5
Cat. no. VP0158

Cover image and illustrations by Lucy Hawkins.
Cover design by Peter Barnfather.
Text design by Fakenham Prepress Solutions.

Printed and bound in Great Britain by
Imprint Digital, Upton Pyne, Exeter.

Contents

WORK

HUMANS

To Alasdair Gray

Glass Work Humans: An Introduction

I T WAS *The Chronicles of Narnia* author CS Lewis who exclaimed that friendship was 'the moment when one person says to another: What! You too? I thought I was the only one'. Hence it genuinely intrigued me to be invited to examine an electrifying body of work produced by the three writers, Paul Cowan, John McKenzie and Tom Gillespie, whose interchangeable, menacing and stimulating voices had absorbed my interest over the past decade.

In *Glass Work Humans*, the three compadres write social realism daydreams in the form of poems, short stories, and longer short stories about vulnerability, insecurities, and assumed shortcomings of humans. The crux is that these perceptions of societal etiquette are not necessarily frailties but have transformed into endearing, enduring hallmarks of the people and places being addressed. This is multi-coloured graffiti for fallacies; regeneration for the disadvantaged.

If serving a dozen years in Police Scotland taught me anything, it was always to pursue the absurdity in crime, and this is something Paul, John and Tom are all sagacious masters at doing. Three writers, each with their own style, all capable of addressing contemporary issues from differing angles. There are stories of how normalised organised crime has become, the fossilised mindsets of "auld polis" officers, and even a dead camel being flogged as steak meat in dives, which sway farcically from the past to the modern day. And then candid contemplation sidles in on issues such as terrorism in the UK, reminding the reader just how fragile existence is.

This collection presents us with heartfelt ambiguity and paints colour into the intimate memories shared with loved ones. A trained eye will ferret out the deep love for fathers, or fatherhood, and then entwine it between lines and words and expressions and absence. There are reasons which become friendships, and when these are coupled with a talent to examine doubts, suspicions, and confusion with a modest shyness, you will find something truly enchanting and looking a lot like the pages between *Glass Work Humans*. Sometimes it pays to be triple-glazed; it keeps the heat in.

Stephen Watt

Glass

PAUL COWAN

Dracula's Hut

SITTING ALONE ON the roof of Dracula's Hut, his eyes scanning the tree-line, Greer could just make out the dark machines populating Jazz Ward's scrapyard like extras from *Jurassic Park*, their twisting metal pistons pumping like baby dinosaur legs. The yard boomed in the background like a battlefield, its giant metal crushers clanking and groaning, its rending production mangling ever more money into Jazz's swollen bank account. No wonder the extravagant prick broke out in Rolexes and top of the range Jags more often than Greer broke out in plooks.

Behind Greer, cars and lorries beat new potholes into Lime Road as they rushed onto some distant wherever, their engines struggling against the weight they had to propel, their lights fading to pinpricks the further they drew away from Dracula's Hut.

Dracula's Hut. The name had been attached to the dilapidated, stone-walled air raid shelter for as long as Greer could remember. He liked the name, although, as he reached into his rucksack and pulled out a bottle of Becks, he'd be hard pushed to tell you why.

The tint from the beer bottle turned Greer's palm green. He placed the butt of his lighter under the bottle top and curled his thumb and forefinger over its body to make a makeshift opener. A firm squeeze from both hands, and a little added torque, sent the lid flying into the trees. No matter. As he lifted the bottle to his parched lips, a rustling noise from behind caused Greer to turn quickly, cold sweat oozing from his pores. Even though he was a man of the forest, and a self-proclaimed Bear Grylls, Greer's level of toughness was limited to the length of his own tongue. As his nerves settled back down, he was surprised to discover he was staring into the eyes of a fox.

"Dinny go near they wee cunts."

His dad's voice echoed in his head.

"The wee bastards huv goat rabies and wull bite the hond aff ye!"

Greer sat alone on the cold, moss-covered roof, silently playing eyeball with the fox, the disease-carrying – according to his dad – stalker and bin tipper who had just invaded his little escape-for-one. He reached back into his rucksack and pulled out a foil-wrapped sandwich. He thought the sudden movement would cause the fox to dart away, but it just sat on its hind legs, cocking its head in languid defiance.

Greer slowly peeled back the foil and placed the sandwich on his lap, never taking his eyes off the fox. He could feel his heart beating – throbbing – through his temples. Nobody knew he was here, no one except the fox, and that thought pleased him. He felt the fastness of the world slow down, as though he'd just been pierced by an anaesthetist's needle. The chaos from last night's domestic between his mum and dad slipped momentarily into the ether.

The mustard from the cheese and ham sarnie singed the hairs in his nostrils, its sharp tang stabbing his senses in potent waves. He looked back to the fox and saw a long slaver like a transparent worm drip from the gulf of its ravenous jaw.

"Fuckin' rabies, am tellin ye," warned his dad from some dark recess.

But Greer saw something else. He wasn't about to approach the feral creature and attempt to make a new friend with claps and cuddles. He just wanted to sit there and be with it. To see what would happen in this hidden oasis. He broke a corner from the sarnie and placed it in his palm, slowly extending it towards the fox, causing it to twitch its head to the opposite side as it cased out Greer's alien gestures. It stood up and slowly inched forward as the morsel of food beckoned its nose in moist twitches. Greer watched in numbed amazement as the fox's sharp-honed whiskers scraped his upturned fingers and patiently nibbled at the food, before opening its jaws softly and carrying the morsel back to its private patch a few feet away, where it ate in slow methodical bites.

The night before, Greer had been awoken by the sound of a loud smash and a thump from downstairs. He recognised the drama straight away. It was 11.30 at night, and Dad had come home from the pub. Mum had pushed his buttons and called him a selfish drunken bastard and the fireworks had exploded. The smash had been the TV as it was lobbed through the living room window, and the thump had been his mum hitting the floor as she tried to remove herself from the line of fire. This was the scene that greeted Greer as he scurried down the stairs and into the living room. His mum was curled up by the side of the couch and he could hear his dad's disturbing whistle from the kitchen, the fan from the cooker humming like a nuclear siren. Greer stepped into the kitchen with eggshell feet. At his approach, his dad looked round slowly, observing him through distant, bloodshot eyes.

"Awrite, son? Am sorry aboot whit ah'm gonny dae, but yer maw's a fuckin' bitch. Ye heard her nigglin' away at me wi that fuckin' horrible rasp ay hers, didn't ye? Ah snapped, son. Am sorry."

The smell of pancreatitis drifted over from Greer's dad like mustard gas. He was jiggling a pan of boiling water over the hob, the blue blaze beneath it more distress flare than flame.

"What's that water for, Dad?" whispered Greer through strangled vocal cords.

"What do ye think it's fur, ya wee fuckin' idiot," his dad exploded across the strewn breakfast bar. "It's gon o'er yer fuckin' maw."

Greer shot from the kitchen like the last leg in a sprint relay, bolting upstairs to his room, where he quickly changed into warm clothes. He stuffed his sleeping bag, his uneaten lunch, his Bear Grylls survival manual, and four bottles of warm Becks from under his bed into his Greenock Morton holdall. With the same frantic speed driven by terror, he exited his broken home and sped towards Dracula's Hut. He had made this familiar trip many times before, under a zillion similar circumstances.

The hollow booms from Jazz Ward's yard pierced holes through Greer's nightmarish memories of the night before and pulled him back onto the moss-smothered roof; back to where the fox sat arched over his food, nibbling away. The sound of the yard and the busy road behind seemed to have no effect on the little hybrid canine muncher. Greer opened a fresh bottle of Becks and took a slow, satisfying glug, the beer cooled to perfection by the night. In that moment, he felt on top of the world. He was free. Free from fathers who slung boiling water over their wives. Free from Rolex-wearing, scrapyard-owning pricks. Free from real life. He was under the stars, drinking a bottle of beer illegally at fifteen and a half years of age, savouring the suds in the bottle so much that when he looked back over at the fox, it was gone. Crumbs and all.

He hadn't even heard it go.

On a Bench

He told me he used to
walk six miles a
day until he
was diagnosed
with type two diabetes
Now he only goes
and collects
his prescription and
buys his papers
amounting to one
mile and booze hasn't crossed
his lips in twelve years

He lights
a Berkeley menthol

He said his son
was 61 and his wife was in
a care home
with Parkinson's
and he goes and
has lunch with
her every day at 2.30
she gets her hair
done on the last Friday
of every month
he goes in as her husband
and leaves as a stranger

He takes a
long laborious draw

He told me he had
a cocker spaniel and it
was 14 when it died
and he will never
get another as
the heartache was too much
and his ankle hurts
because of a botched
operation he had in the navy
where the metal rod
they inserted keeps hitting
the bone
causing arthritis

He holds it
in for at least a minute

He said he and his wife
who he met in the
navy when she was a
wren and he a mechanic
liked to go to Fintry
and he could remember a
time before the whole
village
had electricity
and they played chess
every night below a full moon

Then he
blows out a mint cloud

He told me that most
nights he stares
at the 4 walls
and his wife gets more
visitors than him
and last night
he had beef casserole again
as he made a big
enough batch
on Monday to last him until
Thursday afternoon when
his nephew takes him
to the Co-op
his week's highlight

We watched the vapours
filter into the clear blue sky

I felt I had travelled
my whole
life just to sit
and have a conversation
with him on
a bench in Aberfeldy
he told me it was
their 46th
anniversary today and he
was going home to
get blind drunk

His name was Alan.

Strum

A young girl
strumming away
today on Cockburn
Street sang
'I have no
future as it's tied
up in strings around
my heart'
I looked across at her feet
and she had no
hat for coins
The neon light
from a shop selling
heart attacks
made her look like
the star spangled
banner

I reached into
my pocket for
green but she was
gone
The lights had ceased
flashing and
the world
had slowed down

Now was a
good time for whatever.

Tam's Premature Eulogy

He came back from the dead again

Once a giant of a man
Now a wilting branch being

blown around by the wind
Slapping against the
cold stones
of the steeple and
drowning in the clothes that are
his only defence against
the cuts and digs
being applied by the people
he used to
goad and gash

He still beats the same path
Cobbled stones
neatly laid out for his
calloused feet
Forever glaring downtrodden at
the frayed stitching on his
around the world boots

Spare me some change
Spare me some change
Every day
Spare me some change

No buses to Slamannan cost
twenty pence

Once a giant man and
still a giant man

Coming back from the dead again
so people can silently huddle
and even pen
a premature eulogy.

My Name Is Joe

THE BREEZE FROM the open window cut like blunt razors across my skin. I was a cunt again. It hadn't taken me long to leave the good guy behind to surf on the alcoholic vapours of self-absorption. I was a bottle of Jack Daniels on legs. My self-inflicted hovel had become a trap I couldn't spring, or spring from. The booze was once again my messiah. It was Sunday night and I was at the end of another beautifully blissful binge.

Monday morning would be spent on the outskirts of an alcoholic seizure where I would stare death in the face.

Tuesday I would be buying a ticket for the ghost train that would chug through the heart of my jangling nervous system and pull me through the claustrophobic night.

Wednesday I would be that guy on TV who'd just walked into *The Twilight Zone*: a dead-boned private eye, following myself around and building a lawsuit against my own crumbling life.

Thursday I would be standing in the cereal aisle of the supermarket staring at the Shredded Wheat, thinking the wholegrain goodness visible beneath the microscope was going to cancel out the last thirty years of debauchery.

Friday I would start juggling with the idea of becoming an entrepreneur and having a successful life instead of wading through pools of superglue with cast iron feet.

Saturday I would be dressed in a cut-price Jimmy Cagney suit, screaming, 'Look ma, top of the world!'

Sunday I would be the bomb disposal expert in Syria with the volatile streak, sniffing around for the next level of insanity, because, let's face it, holding my white-hot life in my hands every day just wasn't cutting it for me anymore.

And on Monday the inevitable inner cunt would return for another square go.

I sat vibrating on the settee, gazing at the veins protruding from my arms. I wanted to open them up with a scalpel and climb inside a bottle of bourbon so I could become one with the life-giving elixir. The couch felt like burlap to my fingertips. Small lasers of electricity seemed to zap me every time I tried to lift them.

My eyes had frosted glass stuck to the pupils, giving me a vision of Glencoe with all of its haunting emptiness and desolation but none of its magnificence. My mouth felt clad in copper and drawing pins were glued upright to the surface of my tongue, each one a brutal assassin, happily stabbing into the roof of my mouth.

I could smell my insides and kept looking at my stomach to see if everything inside me hadn't become external and was spreading across my pine wood floorboards like intestinal contagion.

Outside I could hear the bushes rustling and knew it was Them. They had no name but I knew They were out there watching my outline through the slat blinds, fixing special listening devices into the masonry and waiting to murder me in my spiral stairwell. I could hear Them laughing and whispering my name. I drowned them out with my own mantra:

'Kill me or cure me. Kill me or cure me.'

The words sang inside me like the last song at a satanic disco. I had to get to the drinks cabinet. I felt I was going to die right there in the living room, my heart pounding, about to explode. I slowly slid onto the floor and moved like a slug towards the Promised Land, impossibly placed on the north face of an alcoholic Eiger, yet beckoning me like a mermaid; me, the intoxicated mariner. The bottles themselves seemed to hum as the moon's glow lit them up like roman candles. I reached the cabinet by miracle and wrenched open the glass door, cracked from an earlier debacle. The room had started to deep-breathe and was twisting like a mincing machine. I grabbed a bottle and it fought me like an anaconda.

'Kill me or cure me. Kill me or cure me … cure me.'

I managed to get the neck of the bottle to my peeled lips and felt the stinging liquid set fire to my oesophagus. The flames ignited inside me like the flare stack on a petro-chemical plant, causing me to scream. I burned into the night and became an Olympic torch. I had arrived once more. I was back. Death didn't stalk me like it used to. I laughed into its gaping maw. Joe Jekyll had invited in Joe Hyde.

I lifted my passport from the coffee table next to the couch and opened it at my photo. I read the name. Joe Harper, it said. Expiry date 2026. What a load of fucking shit, I thought. I was going to live forever.

They say moments of clarity come at the most absurd times. Some people call them epiphanies. Some say they were touched by the hand of God Almighty. I sat there plotting, plotting to rise like a barbarian, imagining an endless future where my name would be passed around campfires in the dead of night like a baton of hope for the beaten and broken, when something in my chest snapped and I dropped the opened bottle onto the floor. I looked at my passport and asked myself where the fuck I was going to run to this time. The soles of my shoes had touched every pavement in the world looking for what I had in front of me now: an open door. All I had to do was get up and walk through it. I knew I'd find myself on the other side.

I picked up the phone and dialled a number. A woman's voice answered and dropped words into my ear, her dulcet tones a warm shower melting mountains of ice.

'Hello, this is Alcoholics Anonymous. Do you mind telling me your name, and if you have a problem with alcohol?'

Through a forest of tears I hunted down the right words.

'Hello ... yes ... my name is Joe.'

Broken

the strong wind pushes
the swan from the
bank

its shadow goading
it into silver reflection,
its wing broken
and limp yet

pulling through the mudded
rut and crooked ditch

two masks of war
howl in ripping turns and
pelt the broken bird

with twisted glee
and rocks, until the morning
sun has blood sizzling
on its surface.

above dark rapture two
graceful feathers land
on the pond

no ripples spread out
while two wretches
drown in Lucifer's cup.

Breathe

When you get that sudden and
undeniable itch
and you
jump out of your chariot and
rush to look in the
mirror to see if forty years of age
looks different from your
last undeniable itch
and you
throw on last night's
crumpled up and soiled garb
and give a solid fuck you
to the gods of
Persil automatic
and you
tackle the back stairs
and they win
and you're lying like *My Left Foot*
behind the Hoover

and you
reach for the door
which is locked
and you twist
the keys and it's still locked
and you go back to the
first locking position
and the door opens

and you shout
'Fuckin' cuntin' door!'
and
you're running down Oliver Road
and you cross Bells
Meadow
and there's skateboards
and roller blades
and there's
airborne jeans and hoodies
and
you dodge the verbal
gauntlet
and you're running for
your life
and there's nobody
chasing you

but the fear of the
unknown still rises
and a hundred forms of other fears
rise from that
and you see people
you know
and you see people
you love
and they don't see
you
and that just
solidifies the notion that you're
living in your own version
of *The Sixth Sense*

and you see an
underpass
and you're hearing
music
and you make for
cover
and there's a crowd and
they're swaying
and there's
Asda bags
and there's Spirit Of The
Wolf fleeces
and sombreness is
getting passed around like
a smouldering joint
and you're miles away from home
and it's not your home of
bricks and mortar but your home of
the soul

that's untethered and surrounded
by a titanium shield
and
there's a man with no legs in a
wheelchair
and he's punching towards the underpass roof
and he's smiling like he'll never
die
and the busker's
belting out
'Help me get my feet back on
the ground'
and wheelchair man's got

tears on his face
and
an artic lorry
produces thunder from
the road above
and you've
stopped running
and there's no fear
and your breath
in the cold December afternoon
rises like a never ending
nicotine exhalation
and you're
fixated on the legless
human circus that unfolds before
your eyes
and you suddenly know
what you've always known

to just breathe.

Invader

YOU LOOK ACROSS the road and see Marius. Bucket and sponge in hand, staring at his Saab. His Polish Saab. Marius the invader from another country. It's seven o'clock on a Sunday morning and you stand naked, twitching the curtains. Staring at Marius. Marius the boring Polish Saab-washing Sunday morning bastard.

You watch as he kneels. Down at the front right wheel arch. Slowly submerging the sponge into lukewarm soapy liquid.

You want to yank open the curtains and bang hard on the double-glazed bedroom window so Marius will look up and see you standing there. Naked. Exposed to him and the whole Lionthorn Estate. But you don't. Something tells you that would be a drastic mistake. Maybe get you huckled away in a police van and placed on the register. The dirty register.

You look over your right shoulder at Kate. Lying on her front. The covers partially covering her buttocks. You want to imprint your right fist deep into the exposed skin, but you don't. The same something tells you not to. You might break your fingers. Your wanking hand kyboshed. Pamela and her five arthritic sisters sacked. So you squeeze out a silent but violent fart instead and bathe in your own toxic cloud.

You turn back to stare at Marius. Out of sight now at his back brake light. You see his hand sticking out. He's looking at his phone. Can't be texting anyone because he's a social pariah. A job stealer. A sooker of manhoods who drives an extension of his own shrivelled smegmatic manhood. Maybe he's part of a paedophile ring and he's setting up a meeting. Dirty fucker. Marius the paedo.

You notice the methane has died down so you squeeze a little more out. Breathe it in again. You turn back to Kate. Kate with the tight ass. Your favourite docking station. You realise you have certain borderline eccentric issues. You also realise you're an impeccable actor. Worthy of an Oscar. A Golden Globe. A YouTube documentary that would turn you into a forty-five-minute monster if ever your thespian mask were to slip.

You realise the entirety of your left side has gone numb standing at the window. Gawking. You feel your heart murmur. Your knees weaken and you grab onto the windowsill. Waking the dust. It aggravates your asthma and you pray for a full-on attack. Kate stirs behind you and you don't bother looking around. You hear her gentle snores and imagine her drifting back into stage five sleep. REM sleep. Your full left side has pins and needles now and your manhood twitches upwards. Towards an oblivious Marius. Normal Marius. Innocently washing his Saab on a Sunday morning before mass. Marius who lives alone.

You notice the black cat make its ritualistic Zen-like stroll across your driveway. The one you'll be reversing out of yourself in forty-five minutes. En route to the same mass as Marius. Across the good luck line generously donated by the cat. Across town to the house of God. You, the good actor. The atheist.

You walk towards the shower. Go through your morning routine. Let the water wash away the madness. The faulty computer on your shoulders stutters into action. Flashes of Marius the invader and methane fist prints.

You enter the walk-in wardrobe. Breathe in the scent of polished wood. You take down your clerical clothing and dress yourself mindfully. Taking slow breaths. You assume your Lutheran gait and glide sedately downstairs. The morning sun shines through the small piece of holy glass adorning the front door. You adjust your priestly collar. Unlock the copper snib, which feels welcoming against your curled hand.

You hear Kate shout from upstairs. "Is that you away, honey?" You don't bother answering. It gives you a smug sense of power not to.

You reach into your robes. Pull out a packet of Silk Cut. Place one between your lips. You don't light it. You hope other curtain-twitchers are looking at you as you stand there, a rogue angel, poised to light a cancer stick. You exit the drive and thank the cat for trying to balm your glasswork soul. You fallen priest. You breathing piece of carrion.

John McKenzie

Affair

In the cliché of a summer's day I caught you.
Once again, a moment of us existed
Long after the embers had been dusted
And scattered from our hearth.
The fragility of hope we once shared
Blew between the distance
As you sat under a perfect tree
And I leaned against rusted railings.

From the no man's land you placed me in
I saw your glasses resting on your nose
Your head was bowed slightly
And I knew your eyes were focused on the ground
Aware that mine
Were never far from you.

Not once did you look up
Yet you knew where I was and what you were doing
Your capacity to burn smouldered through
The haar of my passivity
And belied the gentle curls of your hair that caught
The fallen blossom from the tree.

Sleep

I held her head while she slept
Her hair was so soft.

I listened to every breath taken
And given back to the world.

I wonder if she knew that I was crying.

Dawn at 8pm

Understanding nothing
Every sense alive and conscious
With an instant fury
That unaccountable loss
Is now a parasite with the desire to breathe.

What chance have we really got?

Graduation Night

Go and run away and write a poem she said
Write how horrible your life is
Or write
How bad you feel.
You are a coward
She said.

You Know I Can See You
and It Frightens You

I put the coffee on the table
And heard the town clock chime midday.

Your bare feet curled
Into the dark blue denim of your jeans

Scattering your poems like autumn leaves
Onto the floor.

Your eyelashes fluttered, and I knew
The world was not broken.

Our fingers were so close
I did not want them to touch.

A Shield to Protect Her from the World

It was three years to the day
He remembered her burgundy leather jacket
How her hair was tied back tightly
Highlighting the eyes that gave nothing away
They did not kiss until a week later
She had invited him round for a coffee
They sat on her sofa
She laughed at how nervous he was, pulled him close
And said it was alright to kiss her.

It hurt, the memory of her hurt.
He tore the page off the calendar and said everything
Was fine.

We Do Not Look Each Other in the Eyes

Her window lay behind
A pair of sombre curtains, that stood like
Statues guarding against the dawn.
She switched off her bedside light
Leaving me in the darkness of her silence.
I heard her breathing get louder until I could no longer
Ignore the fact she was crying.
Her tears fell on our tomb and I offered no resistance
As her stone protectors loomed over me
With their swords drawn.

Scar

I drove to escape you
Over the bridge, over water
Finding one of your favourite views
Gripping the wheel, I saw the permanent bite
Left on my hand by your rage

Where are you? What are you doing?

The oil refinery flamed across a lifeless grey sea
And kept your secrets.

Untitled

Over your bed, the spectre
Of the last six months hung with failed menace.
From behind the curtain, the dawn offered its assistance
As a clouded darkness struck out in anger
Unable to breach the sheath that encased us.
I remembered last night; how your hair fell
Into the shallow of your collar bone
As you slept cooried into my arms.

TOM GILLESPIE

Corpses

O N MY WAY to Buchanan Street Station, I made the unconscious decision to accidentally miss three buses back home, so by the time I finally reached my cousin's house the wake was in full swing. A horrendous 70s pop tune blared out of an open window as I approached, and I could see bodies passing backwards and forwards, in and out of the frame. I felt my stomach lurch, and was half-turning to flee when the door flew open and my cousin stumbled out, ranting at someone behind her in the hall. Seeing me standing there like a bewildered stray dog caught in the headlights of an on-coming juggernaut, she threw up her arms and hollered, 'Dunk!', and then rushed towards me. She was the only person I knew who called me Dunk. She always had, despite my numerous attempts to correct her.

'It's Steven,' I'd insist.

'But Dunk suits you, wee Dunky,' she'd always say and ruffle my hair, or pinch my cheek. I don't know where it came from, but for as long as I could remember she'd driven me nuts with it.

'Hullo, Annie,' I said, bracing myself for impact. In a heartbeat she had me in a vice-like grip, her tree trunk arms squeezing the life out of me until I thought I was going to pass out. And then came the kisses. Launched from puckered, deep crimson, Exocet warhead lips, they rained down over the entire surface area of my face with an almost fatal accuracy. She was no shrinking violet at the best of times, but fully loaded on rocket fuel she was more demonstrative than a WWF champion wrestler.

'Where huv ye been?' she wailed, finally relaxing her grip and allowing me to breathe.

'Glasgow,' I wheezed, trying to wriggle free from her bear hug. 'Ye know, uni an that.' I noticed both her eyes were bloodshot. 'Sorry about Aunty Mary. How did it go today, wi the funeral?'

'Aww ...' she said, gazing skyward, 'she'll be up there soon enough, swingin' wae yer faither.'

I forced a smile and tried to wipe the thought from my mind.

'It's a shame yer mithir couldnae come doon,' she said, returning to earth.

'She's still no up to travellin,' I said, 'but she sends her love. She wanted me to check that her flowers arrived okay.'

She didn't hear me. She was busy fumbling in her oversized handbag, trying to balance a glass in one hand and a cigarette in the other.

'Hawd that a minute, will ye,' she said, ramming her drink against my chest, causing some to spill down the front of my shirt. When she re-emerged it was with a fistful of notes.

'Nip doon the shoap and git some mair supplies,' she said, waving the money in my face. She then reeled off a long list of intoxicants as though running through a stock audit at Agnew's.

A bottle a Teachers – no, better make that 2
2 bottles a Smirnoff
A bottle of Cinzano Bianco, fur Noreen next door
8 cans a Tennents
8 cans a 70 Shillin
A bottle a ginger – Irn Bru or lemonade, it disnae matter
80 Lambert an Butler
An whitivir you want

'I'm no sure I'll be able to carry aw that,' I said, trying to commit the list to memory. But she was already back inside the house roaring at the top of her lungs for somebody to turn the music up. I set off for the corner shop with a deep sense of foreboding in the pit of my still-knotted stomach.

❧

The feeling was still there when I got back with my bulging bags of booze, but Annie wasn't. It didn't seem like anybody was. The music had stopped and the entire house was wrapped in a suspicious quiet.

'Hullo?' I called, trying to locate where the merry mourners were holed up. Getting no answer, I ventured further down the hall. And then I spotted Uncle Davie, stranded halfway up the stairs, with his sticks lying spread-eagled at the bottom.

'Are you alright?' I asked, downing my bags and rushing to help him. I took his arm to support his weight and felt him sink into me.

'Am loast,' he said, dropping his head into his hands. My relationship with Uncle Davie had never been easy. He'd always treated me with suspicion, or borderline contempt, especially after I got into university, the first in the family. It was nothing he'd say directly to my face, but it was always there, under the surface. I'm not sure what it was about. Maybe he'd always wanted something better for himself and his own kids, but none of them had quite managed to crawl out of the hole they'd dug for themselves; or that fate had dug for them.

'You're doing okay, Davie,' I said, trying to reassure him. The words sounded hollow even to me.

'Whit dae ah dae noo?' he asked, looking at me through the haze of prolonged intoxication.

'I suppose ye jist huf tae plough on,' I replied. It was the best I could do. To be honest, I'd never experienced grief before, aside from the loss of our terrapin when I was nine, so I was pretty clueless about what you should or shouldn't say to someone whose whole world had fallen from under them. Uncle Davie shrugged and mumbled something under his breath.

'Come on,' I said. 'Ye cannae sit here aw night. For one thing yer blockin the route to the loo.' Taking his arm again I tried lifting him, but he refused to budge.

'Ah kin dae this masel,' he protested, shrugging off my help and forcing himself to his feet. Slowly he shuffled downstairs and into the living room. I followed him, but when I tried to lower him back into his armchair, he pushed my hand away again.

'Where's ma fuckin drink?' he bellowed, staring at me with accusatory eyes. I scanned the empty glasses and cans, and other assorted debris around his chair.

'Let me get you one. Beer?' Secretly I hoped he'd go for the soft drink option.

'Beer?' he slurred, sarcastically. 'Who the fuck drinks that pish?'

I lifted out a new bottle of whisky from the bag, poured a large measure into one of his filthy tumblers, and topped it up with Irn Bru. I remembered from a previous tirade that this was his preferred mixer. Handing him the glass, he guzzled it down. Within seconds he was dead to the world, his snores like a pneumatic drill working its way through a particularly stubborn section of tarmac.

I carried the bags through to the kitchen and dropped them in the doorway. The room was a state. There were filthy dishes and discarded bottles and cans covering almost every square inch of surface. The kitchen table was strewn with half-eaten sandwiches and biscuits, and I counted at least half a dozen overflowing ashtrays. Every cupboard door lay wide open and dirty pots and pans were piled up in a foul-smelling, overflowing sink. It looked as though they'd been there for weeks, rather than a few hours. I unpacked the booze and fags and squeezed them into a space on the floor by the dog bowls.

'The dog,' I suddenly remembered. 'Where's the dog?' In a previous incarnation, when she was still functioning as a living, breathing human being, my cousin used to breed Alsatians; enormous, feral creatures that would take over her house and hunt me down in rabid, blood-thirsty packs every time I paid a visit. I was terrified of them, and rightly so. They'd been known to take lumps out of the neighbours and, on one memorable occasion, had put the postman in hospital for a month. Now Annie only kept the one dog, so old it was riddled with arthritis. That didn't stop it meaning business though. It was a right tough bastard, and if it bared its teeth at you, you ran like fuck. Which was exactly what I felt like doing right now. With a spiralling sense of fear and loathing, I breathed in a lungful of stale air and went to find the rest of the funeral party.

Gently, I pushed open the door to the front room, or the parlour, as Aunty Mary always called it. Inside was dark and gloomy, and for a moment I struggled to see what or who was in there. As my eyes adjusted, my cousin's substantial frame emerged from the shadows, followed by her equally proportioned sister Rhona. They were both leaning over a dark wooden casket, with the other guests gathered around them, nodding, whispering, and craning their necks to see.

Oh, Jesus Christ, I thought. She's still here.

Suddenly Rhona threw her arms in the air. 'Ma Mammy!' she cried, and started rocking the coffin from side to side, almost knocking it off its stand. Annie stood beside her, sobbing quietly, her thick arms wrapped around her sister.

The dog – *that's where it was!* – sat by Annie's side, a canine guardian at the gates of Hades, its teeth retracted but its eyes ablaze.

I approached a neighbour lingering at the back of the room.

'I thought the funeral was today?' I whispered, not quite willing to accept what I was seeing.

'They postponed it til the moarnin,' he rasped, adding, 'They wurny ready to let go.'

Rhona spotted me hiding in the dark.

'Aww, Steven … moan,' she said, inviting me to join them ringside.

I shook my head and pushed back as far as I could into the rear wall.

'Moan and see yer wee aunty,' Rhona implored again, holding out a shaking hand.

I could feel the panic rise in my throat and my body spiral into flight mode.

'Go on son,' the neighbour said, digging me in the ribs with his elbow. 'Go on.'

I found myself slowly edging towards the coffin, my eyes fixed on the hypnotically lurid 70s carpet beneath my feet.

'There she is,' Rhona said with a tearful, quivering smile.

As I leaned in and peered over the top of the coffin, the dog growled and jumped at me, its paws scratching my chest through my just-bought Joy Division T-shirt.

'Senga!' Annie hollered, and the dog sat back down, obediently. I grabbed at my T-shirt, checking for blood. Nothing. Just a couple of puncture holes. Wee bastard.

'Huv ye ever seen her sae peaceful?' Annie's tone had switched back to maudlin. I took a deep breath and returned to the coffin.

Aunty Mary's head and shoulders were visible above a tightly-wrapped silken shroud that covered the rest of her tiny, emaciated frame. This was the first time I'd seen a dead body and it was everything I'd feared, and more. The skin on Mary's face had sunk back against the skull, as though the life had been hoovered out of her, and what was left no longer resembled a human being. I stared at the death mask for a moment trying to locate my aunt's features in the shrivelled remains, but there was nothing left of her. She was gone.

'I need a drink,' I said, and blundered through to the kitchen, where I poured myself a large whisky, downing it in one. By the time I was halfway through a Tennents chaser, the music had started up again. This time it was Abba's 'Mamma Mia', and following a premature cacophony of 'how can I resist ya!', the track suddenly switched to 'Super Trooper', before switching again, and again, skipping through Abba's greatest hits, until finally the familiar riff of 'Dancing Queen' kicked in.

'Oh, good God,' I muttered under my breath, quickly tanking the rest of my can.

Annie appeared in the doorway, wailing at the top of her lungs.

'Yer auntie loved this one, Dunk,' she slurred, her drink swilling and spilling over the side of her glass. 'Moan gee us a wee dance.'

'Ah'm just havin a quiet moment to myself here, Annie,' I said, holding up my can and praying she'd quickly give up on me. But before I could contemplate escape, she was all over me again, her arms encircling and then crushing me like a starved boa constrictor. I tried to fight her off but she was too strong.

'Friday night and the lights are on!' she roared in my ears as she dragged me back down the hall.

The rest of the party had returned to the living room, and I was relieved when Annie pushed me in to join them, rather than hauling me back to the tomb of Tutankhamun.

Everyone was on their feet, dancing – or trying to; an epileptic orgy of flailing arms and legs. Every so often somebody would collide into somebody else.

A freshly-woken Uncle Davie was in the thick of it, almost bent double, shuffling from side to side, an inch or two at a time, shouting and laughing hysterically. Annie shoved me into the centre of this haphazard circle and pulled and pushed my shoulders so violently I gave in.

I'm no dancer, and Annie isn't any better. But under the influence of alcohol she's a bloody liability. She went for a spin and almost toppled over Uncle Davie, who was now crawling around on his hands and knees and calling out repeatedly, 'Where's ma drink, Annie? Where's ma fuckin drink?' The dog was now beside itself, jumping around, growling and snapping at Davie's backside, thinking he was either play fighting or proposing a bit of hanky panky. Over in the corner, Annie's sister was dancing at half speed with one of the neighbours. She had him in a clinch, and while she swayed, writhed, and ground her voluminous hips against his trouser leg, she slowly worked him backwards towards the wall. In one swift and well-practised move, she forced his arms back and lunged at his face, creating what appeared to be a perfect vacuum around his sphincter-shaped mouth. I suddenly felt queasy and edged back towards the door.

Annie chose that moment to stumble into the record player, and with a loud rip the needle tore across the vinyl and the music stopped.

'Wait a minute,' she slurred. 'Start again.' And after a few more failed attempts to relaunch the song, with the needle screeching across the surface and the speakers almost falling off the sideboard, the Dancing Queen was back in the room.

'This one's fur Mammy.' Turning the volume up as far as it would go, Annie grabbed her sister's hand and they took off together. One of the neighbours caught hold of Rhona's waist and the entire funeral party formed an impromptu conga line, weaving their way in and out the chairs.

'Pit oan Matt Munro, Annie!' Uncle Davie roared. 'She prefert Matt!'

Annie ignored him. 'Moan, Dunk,' she said, hauling me in, as the line snaked out the door and down the hall towards the parlour, the dog in its element, yapping and circling, ducking in and out a forest of legs.

'You can dance!' the line wailed in unison, as it disappeared into the parlour, dragging me with it.

'Having the time of your life!' Annie croaked again, our conga line now encircling the coffin. Leaning over, she reached in and lifted the corpse halfway out of its box. 'Look, she's loving it!' she shouted above the noise, swinging her mother from side to side in time with the music. 'And when you get a chance! Moan, Mary Mam, you sing it.' Annie lifted the body further out the casket. Suddenly the dog leapt up, almost toppling the coffin, and began licking frantically at the corpse's pale puckered skull.

'Come on, Annie, for fuck's sake!' I cried out in horror, unable to contain myself any longer. But she was too far gone to hear my plea.

'You are the dancing queen!' Rhona chorused, and together with her sister they held a withered grey arm aloft, making the body wave back at the mourners as the song continued to belt out its happy, uplifting melody.

'Dae ye want a wee swally, Mammy?' Annie asked, and pressed her glass to the corpse's lips. Not waiting for an answer, she tipped it into her dead mother's mouth until the whisky dribbled out and down her chin.

'Having the time of your life!' she repeated, about three lines too late.

'An maybe a wee puff as well,' one of the neighbours interrupted, holding up his cigarette. A furious Annie thumped it out of his hand, sparks flying in all directions.

'Don't dae that!' she roared. 'That's fuckin' disrespectful.' The flummoxed neighbour rushed to extinguish the embers before the whole place went up in flames.

Shifting her position, Annie took her dead mother's withered face in her hands and kissed both sunken cheeks.

'Ma poor wee mammy!' she cried, breaking down again. But not for long. Wiping her nose with the heel of her hand and sniffing loudly she was soon back on song.

'Watch the screen, you are the dancing queen!' Joined again by Rhona, the sisters carried out a macabre version of pass the parcel with the lifeless body until the song came to a juddering halt.

❧

I shook my head. It was too much. Leaving them to it, I made my escape while they fought over whose turn it was to hold the corpse. And as I retreated up the path, I heard another screech of the needle and Abba's signature tune start up for the umpteenth time.

Waiting at the bus stop to take me back to the safety of the city, the anger and revulsion I felt at my cousins' behaviour gave way to a realisation that, like it or not, I was bonded to them. We belonged to a shared genealogy that neither I nor they would ever be able to shake off. It was pointless to think I wasn't like them, or that somehow I could run away from them and be a better or more complete person. They were a part of me and I was a part of them; thoughts of escape were futile. I smiled and laughed out loud, wondering if all families dealt with grief as well as we did. Despite the absurdity and horror of the afternoon, I knew that somewhere buried deep within my genetic blueprint, I carried the same hope and expectation that when I lay cold and withered in my coffin, my future sons and daughters, nieces and nephews would allow me one final dance and a wee dram before sticking me in the incinerator and tipping what was left into a hole in the ground.

'But not Dancing Queen,' I thought. 'That would be fucking disrespectful.'

Sleeper

ALICE NUDGED HER husband in the ribs. 'John! You're snoring!' John grunted, was quiet for a moment, and then started back up again. Alice sighed. She'd lost count of the number of disrupted nights she'd had since he got back. She'd always found it difficult to readjust whenever he returned from offshore, but this time the physicality of his presence was overwhelming. She could barely breathe. After a few more minutes tossing and turning, attempting sleep, Alice finally gave up and padded downstairs to the cool, relative quiet of the kitchen. As she waited for the kettle to boil, the cat slinked in through the flap. Alice pulled at its tail affectionately.

'Where have you been?' she said quietly. The cat gave her a look as if to say *none of your business*. Alice ignored him and emptied a sachet of food into his bowl. The cat took one sniff and slinked back out. Alice watched his tail disappear into the night.

'Suit yourself.'

Grabbing her mug, Alice slumped down at the table. She could still hear John snoring upstairs. All she wanted was five minutes peace, but the droning and wheezing was louder than the tea swirling around her mouth and down her throat. She retreated to the living room and closed the door. Pulling a chair over to the window, Alice peered out into the street. The world always seemed so simple in the dead of night. She spotted her cat in the garden opposite squaring up to the neighbour's tom. They circled for a moment and then chased each other around the side of the house. Alice let out a long weary sigh and rested her mug on the window sill.

She had thought about leaving John more than a few times. She'd even got as far as packing a bag and loading the car, but as she'd driven down the street, she'd become more and more agitated, and by the time she'd reached the lights at the top of the town, she'd found herself in the throes of a full-blown panic attack. It had been so bad she'd had to park the car and walk all the way home, dragging her bulging holdall behind her.

Leaning out of the chair, Alice glanced up the street. There was something moving in the shadows. She wiped the condensation from the window and pressed her face against the glass. A figure emerged from the gloom. He was naked, walking slowly up the centre of the road. As he drew nearer, Alice could make out more of his features. He was middle-aged with a balding pate and a small paunch that flopped over the top of his groin. He was staring straight ahead, his eyes fixed on an unseen point in the far distance. His walking, Alice noted, was unusual. He'd pause before taking a step, his bare foot hovering just above the surface of the road. Alice hoped he wouldn't stand on a sharp stone, or worse, a nail.

Approaching Alice's front garden, the naked man raised his left arm and held it above his head. He stopped when he reached her front gate. Alice pulled back a little, peering at the man's nakedness through a gap in the curtain. The man looked up and stared directly at her. For a second she thought he was going to continue up her path – and then what? – but after a pause that seemed to hang in the air forever he dropped his arm, his foot fell forward, and he walked on by. Alice watched him to the end of the cul-de-sac, where he – inexplicably – disappeared into the shadows. Alice briefly wondered what his wife must be thinking, waking in the night to an empty pillow, an empty bed, an empty life.

Upstairs, Alice took one last look out the bedroom window, but the naked man was nowhere to be seen. She wondered what she'd say to John about him in the morning, but was there really any point in saying anything? He'd only make a fuss, and he probably wouldn't believe her anyway. Climbing back into bed, Alice ran her eyes over the flat expanse of her husband's partially-exposed back. In the early years of their marriage he'd loved having her massage his back. His shoulders too. It calmed him. Alice smiled at the memory and pulled the bedsheet up around her throat. John had stopped snoring now and was breathing gently, his large frame heaving up and down, like the ebb and flow of a returning tide. Alice tucked in behind him, pushed her hand between his knees, and for the first time in days, fell into a deep and restful sleep.

Crime Scene

FRANKIE COMES IN, soaked to the marrow and with a face like a smacked arse.

'Whit's up wae you?' I say to him, but he just sits there like a big droont numpty.

He points at my glass.

I search my pockets for a note. 'I'll get these.' I buy him a half and a half and he downs both in one. And then I ask him again.

'I finally done it,' he says, and then starts wrestling with one of his half-arsed roll ups.

I offer him my own pack, to little resistance.

He takes two or three long drags and blows the smoke into my face.

'Done whit?' I ask, but it's like trying to get a confession out the Pope. He taps the bar with his glass. Fuck it. If that's what it takes. I rise and get him another.

I wait patiently while he finishes off his 80 shilling and then I give him a nudge.

'So?'

'I've done something really stupid, Tam,' he says, wiping the froth from his top lip.

'What now?' I'm trying hard no tae yawn.

No reply.

'Frank!'

'It's Mary.'

'What about her?'

'She pushed me too far.' He shakes his head and half a gallon of rainwater pours from his anorak hood.

'Oh for fuck's sake, Frankie. You two are like a stuck fucking record. Don't tell me she's banging that wee ned fae the Drum again?'

He ignores my remark, picks up my cigarettes, and carries on. 'We were huvin' a row, the usual shite, an' she went tae bed in the huff.' He lets out a long sigh. 'I was ragin' wae her. She calt me a spongin', lazy strip o' shite.'

'Well, that's exactly what you are my friend, so good on you, Mary girl.' I toasted Frankie's wife in absentia.

'I lost it,' he says.

'Ye didnae thump her, did ye?'

'No.'

'Thank fuck fur that, coz she'd put you in the fucking Western Infirmary if you tried that shite.'

'I did somethin' worse.'

'How d'yae mean?'

He shook his head again.

'Frankie, for fuck's sake,' I'm losing my patience wae him by this point.

'I've dun her in,' he says, calm as you like.

I try to spot his usual cheeky sneer, or a gleam in his eye, but he still looks like a slab of meat in a mortuary.

'You've whit?' I say, lowering my voice.

He draws his finger across his throat.

'You've bumped her?'

He nods and stubs out his fag.

'Come on, stop messing wae me.'

'I told ye, I was fumin' an' I totally lost it.' He lights up another.

'Jesus Christ, you are pissing me about, aren't you?'

He says nothing.

'Fuck's sake, Frank. If you're fucking with my nut, I'll do *you* in.'

'I'm no jokin', Tam. She's lying up there now, stiff as a fucking board. I put a pillow over her face and everything just kind of stopped.'

'Oh, mother of God.' I can't believe what I'm hearing. I shake my head. 'You fucking idiot.'

He holds up his glass again.

'Aye aye,' I nod. Suddenly I feel it's *me* that needs a fucking drink.

When the barman's done, Frankie takes a couple of long slugs of his pint and rests the glass in his lap.

'What in the fuck got into you?' I feel like punching him in the face.

'I'm tellin' ye, I just lost it.'

'I fucking lose it all the time with Annie, but I don't fucking suffocate her, ya stupid cunt.' I feel the panic setting in. 'And poor Mary, I know she's a bit of a rat's arse of a wife, but even she disnae deserve that.'

'I just saw red, and then she was deed,' he says, like he was reading the fucking form at the bookies.

'Are you sure?' I say, though Christ knows why.

'She rolled aboot for a bit and then when she stopped kickin', I got her make-up mirror out of her handbag and checked to see if she was still breathin'.'

'Fucking hell! What are you, some kind of Jack the fucking psycho?'

I sit there in stunned silence for a few minutes staring at the rows of whisky bottles behind the bar. But then he stands up, looking like he's about to do a runner.

'No you fucking don't,' I say, and pull him back down onto his stool. 'Forget that pish, you need to go to the cops, right now.'

'I canny,' he says, and tries to get back up. I push him back down.

'Frankie, I'm serious, you have to. It'll only make things worse if you don't.'

'I canny go back inside, Tam,' he says. 'They'll fucking take me apart in there.'

'I hope they fucking do, you bastard. And now I'm a bloody accessory, thank you very fucking much. So if you don't turn yourself in then I'll have to do it for you, or they'll bang me up wae ye, sure as eggs are fucking eggs.'

'I just canny dae it,' he says again, like a fucking Punch and Judy show.

I empty what I have in my pockets onto the bar and count out enough for a couple more pints.

'Listen,' I say, my head swimming with booze. 'I'll come wae ye. I could be a friendly witness. I'll tell them she battered you, and then they'll think it was self-defence. You'll probably get a non-custodial.'

'Wae ma track record, I don't think so,' says Frankie.

'I could even gie ye a smack in the pus, if ye like, to make it look authentic.'

He takes my arm and leans in close. 'Wid ye really dae that fur me, Tam?'

'Look,' I say to him. 'I know you're now a cold-blooded wife-killer and all that, blah, blah, blah, but we're still pals, right?'

'Always, ya cunt,' he says.

'Right, so, you need to do as I say. Make this the last drink, and then we go up to Stuart Street, okay?'

'Okay. But what about Mary?' he says.

'What about her?'

Before he can reply, we're rudely interrupted by a loud roar coming from the entrance.

'Frankie!'

I spin round on my stool. There, standing in the doorway, blocking out most of the light, is his dearly beloved, looking about as dead as a rampaging rhino.

'Where's the fucking tin foil?' she hollers at him.

'Sorry, Mary darlin', just popped in for a swifty an' bumped into wee Tam here.'

'I'll gee ye a fucking swifty. Home, now!' Then she sees me. 'Hello Tam, how's Annie keepin'?' she says, forcing a smile and dropping her voice a couple of decibels.

Frankie climbs off his stool. 'Thanks for the bevvies,' he says, grinning at me. 'The ciggies too.' And he taps the box he'd managed to pinch from under my nose while I was wrestling with my conscience earlier. I try to take a swipe at him, but I lose my balance and nearly fall off my stool.

'That's the last fucking time,' I say to myself, as I watch the two of them shouting and swearing at each other, Mary brutally manhandling Frankie out of the pub into the cold light of day. As the beer begins to settle and the room stops spinning, and I realise I don't have enough money left for my bus fare home, I finally understand the true value of having a total cunt for a best friend.

Monogamy

I MUST HAVE put it down on the bedside table, or maybe I left it next to the sink. He said it was putting him off, like I was some kind of meal he didn't want to eat any more. I knew I'd leave it. I should have put it in my bag or slipped it into my skirt pocket before we started. I can't believe my own stupidity sometimes. I just forgot all about it and didn't realise I'd left it until it was too late. When I pressed the bell for my stop, I noticed the white line where the sun hadn't turned the skin brown. It's a couple of blocks from the stop to the house, so I had time to concoct and practise my story, not too many words, just enough to convince Dave and stifle any doubts. But the house was empty. I went from room to room, looking for him. I checked upstairs but he wasn't there. I opened the wardrobe and his clothes were gone, and his drawers were empty, his toiletries removed from the shelf. I searched for a note but there was none and the floor opened up in front of me.

I'd used soap and hot water to work it over the knuckle. It dropped into the sink and almost vanished down the plughole.

'Come on,' he'd said. 'What are you doing in there?'

'Just hiding my shame, darling,' I felt like screaming through the door.

And then, when it was over, I showered, dressed, and rearranged my hair, as though nothing had happened. On the bus home, I could still feel him inside me and I felt sick to my stomach.

How did Dave know? Perhaps he didn't and he was just as tired of me as I was of him. I tried ringing him, over and over, but it went to voicemail each time. I stripped the bed and vacuumed the carpet. I don't know why. Perhaps I was looking for some kind of closure that wouldn't come.

He called late. I was still awake, waiting for the phone to ring. His voice was different, short of breath and monosyllabic. He said he would be round for the rest of his stuff in the morning. A chance to talk. I said I wouldn't be in and hung up, instantly regretting it. I picked up the receiver again but he was gone. I opened a bottle of wine and didn't stop until it was empty.

The flat is silent. The sound of air clicking through my teeth annoys me, so I turn on the radio. Something about an explosion in Madrid and bodies scattered across a station platform. I turn it off and return to the bedroom. I lie out on the bare mattress and close my eyes. Tomorrow I will bag and bin what's left of him, and go back for my wedding ring. If nothing else, it's worth its weight in gold.

Kramer's Dolls

You must remember the Kramers. They lived at number 23, you know, just up the road. Mind you, there's no reason why you should remember them, they weren't exactly what you'd call neighbourly. There was this one time I bumped into Mrs Kramer in the chemist. She was in front of me in the queue. I wasn't sure if it was her at first but when she was leaving, I stopped her to say hello. I don't think she had any idea who I was. She just stared at me with a face like fizz and went off on her merry way. The cheek of it. And he was the same; never looked the road you were on. Anyway, I never saw hide nor hair of them again, until I found out she'd passed away. To be honest, it didn't surprise me because she was like death warmed up most of the time anyway; pneumonia, apparently. But it must have been terrible for him though. I can't imagine what I'd do if my Frank dropped off his perch.

Anyway, where was I? Oh aye, about two or three weeks after finding out about Mrs Kramer, the queerest thing happened. These wee dolls began appearing in Mr Kramer's front window. At first it was only a few, all lined up along the inside of the sill. They were strange wee things. They looked as though they'd been hand-sewn out of cotton and silk and the like; wee men and women, beautifully dressed in dinner suits and colourful party dresses and shiny black boots and shoes. The detail was immaculate. Every day, they'd be rearranged in a different order, or a new doll would join the group. It wasn't long before the whole window was full of them, tucked up together along the sill and filling out the frame above. People in the street would stop and natter about them and speculate on poor Mr Kramer's state of mind. What was it all in aid of? The man was clearly developing some kind of unhealthy obsession. The weans in the street started calling him the witch doctor, like the dolls were full of voodoo or some such awful thing. And the McAllister boy – you know, daft John from the Gallowgate, his lad – he swore blind he saw them moving about on their own one night on his way home, but between you and me, that boy's never off the smokies and I don't know what he's blethering about half the time.

There was definitely something unsettling about them though, all huddled up like that. The way they stared out at you as you walked past. We were fortunate because we couldn't see them from here, but poor old Mrs Kilpatrick over at number 13, she was so feart of them she ended up keeping her curtains shut.

But then, last Tuesday morning, things took a turn for the worse. I was on my way back from the Tesco Metro with my shopping and I stopped by his gate to rest my arms for a minute. I wasn't going to look, and I wish I hadn't, because I just couldn't believe what I was seeing. The dolls were still there, right enough, lined up as usual, but all their heads were missing, like they'd been cut with a knife or snipped off at the neck with a pair of scissors. It was quite horrific, but it gets worse. When I looked over his garden wall, his front lawn was littered with them. There must have been over thirty wee severed heads, scattered everywhere. The poor wee lambs, how could he do such a thing? There were even a couple lying in the road. I was going to pick them up but I just couldn't go near them, their sad beady eyes staring up at me. It makes me shudder to think. He must've gone mental. I was ready to knock on his door, it upset me so much, but then I thought better of it and left him to it.

If you want my honest opinion, it doesn't surprise me that he went doolally. I never had that much time for either of them, but him, he was a piece of work. I felt sorry for her because he always seemed so dour. He must have been an absolute misery to live with, especially if he was prone to that sort of nonsense. No, definitely not the sort of people you'd want round for dinner or drinks or anything like that. But having said that, I wouldn't like to think of him suffering in there on his own. I wouldn't wish that on anyone, not even him. I might just drop a wee note through his door tomorrow, just to let him know that, well, at the very least, if he needs anything from Tesco or town, I'm in every Tuesday morning. It'd be easy enough to bring it back on the bus. What do you think, do you think I should?

Craw

W I WUR UP the auld Carron Brig Road, yae know near the Dows ferm, huvvin wan ae' oor usual barneys. Ah swear tae goad, ivry time we get in the caur, we end up shoutin' 'n swearin' it wan anithir. Wur is predictable is git oot, so wae ur. At least we wur in the middle a naewhere so naebdae could hear the shite that wis comin' oot a' his mooth.

Onywaeys, so there wi ur in the howls a nothin' gi'in it laldy, 'n him drivin' through the snaw like a bampot possessed, when somethin' stoats aff the windae. Jesus Christ, it wis that loud I thoat a tree hid come doon oan tap ae us. He slams oan the brakes, and the caur skiteit right acroas the road. We goat a fair fright, so we did. We'd nae idea whit the hell it wis, but there wis a big crack acroas the windscreen. I telt him tae go and hiv a look. And you know whit he sayed? He sayed: 'It's snawin'.' It's snawin', for fuck's sake, peel me a bloody grape. Ah thumped him again, and efter anither roon o' huffin' and puffin', he pits his coat oan. He wis pure ragin' so he wis, but I mean tae say, ye cannny jist drive awa' withoot knowing whit ye've jist hit. Wur human beins. Wur no bloody monsturs.

I cloacked him in the mirror, lumberin' up the road like a big bloody doh-heed. Then the next thing he stoaps by a wee lump in the snaw. He wis there fir ages, jist bloody starin' at whitever it wis. Whit in God's name wis he daein? Ah wis aboot tae get oot 'n gie him a herd kick up the erse, when he stoats the lump wae his fit, an horror o' horrors, the thing sterts movin' an flappin' aboot. Next thing, he's jumpin' up and doon oan it, huvvin a right go. He wis pure dementit. But yi know whit he did next? Ah couldny believe whit ah wis seein'. He kneels doon and picks the bloody thing up, swings it oor his heed 'n lobs it intae a hedge it the side ae the road. The man's awa', ta ta, so he is.

When he gets back in the caur, he jist sits there staring oot the windae, and when ah ask him whit it wis, he gies me the strangest look, 'n says:

'Craw.'

Then he starts the caur, turns it roon, an we drive hame withoot anithir word between us.

Ye know, when ah think aboot it, we never spoke aboot that night again, an ahm no sure why ahm even thinking aboot it the noo. Ah s'pose I'm aye remindit by that crack in the winscreen that he refused to hiv repairt. Or mebbe it's every time ah cloack that funny look oan his face, the same wan he wis wearing efter he pit that poor burd oot its misery, ah feel a wee bite in ma belly, like sherp teeth … or a beak.

Work

PAUL COWAN

Vinegar Stroke

M Y INDUCTION WAS in five minutes. For a job I didn't want but couldn't afford to refuse. FTV *fucking* Aceweld, a germ-ridden boagle dangling from the nose of Glenrothes. Talking of which ...

"Excuse me. Scud Book? Yer name's Scud Book, isn't it?"

His patter was second-hand, but his sweat was fresh, the concentrated odour from his oxters forming a cloud around my head.

He laughed, the sound of it scraping the ceiling, as though I'd just kicked him in the knackers.

"Sorry," he said. "Ah'm just pullin' yer leg, eh?" He stuck out a hand. "Eric Whitehead."

He had a putty-like protrusion that sat on the edge of his nose like a rock tipping over a cliff. I couldn't make eye contact because of an invisible nasal magnet that kept drawing me into its peaks and valleys. Let the mountain come to Mohammed.

I shook his hand vigorously, wishing I had broon sauce smeared on it. "Ross McCallum," I replied, my eyes wide in mock wonder. "Christ, yer patter's good. Ye must have been up till three in the mornin' scratchin' that stuff oot. Whit time dis yer show start at the Fringe?"

"Ohhhhh," he said. "Good stuff, Ross the Doss. Looks like ah've a little competition on the factory floor. But remember this: ah'm a precision knife-thrower, an' wan o' ma honed blades might find its way in between yer ribs wan o' these days. So ah'd recommend ye grow eyes in the back o' yer neck, son. Pronto."

He spat onto the ground, a thick green foam that parted like bubbles in the bath. When I looked back up he was gone, disappeared into the huge factory with its blue flashing lights and deep rumbles. I felt I was standing over the King's Cross Tube station at rush hour, seven million drones commuting into its heart to earn a crust. And there *I* was – at FTV *fucking* Aceweld – to do the very same thing.

And yet here I was again. What was it Elton John called it? The Circle Of Life? Circle Of Pish, more like. What was I doing back here? Hadn't bankruptcy, divorce, and debilitating self-hatred not been humiliating enough? Fuck it. At the end of the day it was a job I still didn't want, but still couldn't afford to refuse.

"Ross McCallum? Ross McCallum!"

When I lifted my head, I found myself staring into the cleavage of a middle-aged woman with a lop-sided name tag.

"Hi, Brenda," I said, wearily. "Ah was tryin' to read yer name there but yer tag wis aw squint. Ah'm Ross McCallum, Ross fae Fawkirk, hame o' the Kelpies, ken? An' dinnae forget the wheel that looks nothin' like a wheel." I laughed. Brenda didn't. "Follow me," she snorted, and led me into a cramped, trapezium-shaped room where I was introduced to Karl, FTV *fucking* Aceweld's so-called safety officer, who was going to take me through the company's safety do's and don'ts.

Karl was no motivational speaker. Boots could have sold his voice over the counter and sent their diazepam supplies back to Hoffmann-La Roche. I fought to stay with him as he guided me through two hours of unbearable dullness. He could have been reciting the lyrics to the *Sesame Street* theme song for all I knew. Or cared.

An indefinable melody filtered through the warning-covered walls. It sounded like lift music, a relic twisting the turntables of time in a dusty loft. Or maybe I was dreaming, imagining myself being serenaded to the sea-bed by a malevolent mermaid. Each time I floated back to the surface, Karl was there, staring at me, *through* me, his lips on auto-pilot, the script not yet done.

"So, Ross," he said, reaching the final paragraph, "are you aware of Aceweld's stellar safety record since I took the reins? I like to get involved with the boys on the shop floor when I can and see if there's any way we can improve the conditions."

I wanted to say, 'Well, Karl, if ye kin stretch yer mind back tae when ah wis here afore, ye'll remember ye wur the *worst* safety officer on the planet, who did nothin' but spout fabrications o' the truth fur aw the oors ye wur awake.' But I didn't. Instead, I said: "Absolutely, Karl. I used to watch you, you know, hovering about the factory with your safety wand, turning potential catastrophes into no-lost-time incidents. You're the Mother Teresa of the safety world – no doubt about it."

Karl nodded, taking my bullshit at its two-faced value. "I like you, Ross," he said. "I didn't before. I think we're going to get on. How would you feel about being my eyes and ears on the front line? If anyone steps out of place, you assess the situation and report straight back to me. What do you say?"

"Ye want me tae be a grass."

The colour fell from Karl's face. "No, no, no, not at all," he sputtered, back-peddling with all the finesse of a drunken Bradley Wiggins. "I was just trying to get you involved in running a tidy ship, because at the end of the day, eh? ... at the end of the day ... listen, how about I play you the safety video to round off the induction?"

Karl inserted a DVD into a player you would have got change for in a pound shop and switched off the lights. In the darkness, I could hear him breathe through his nose, which only served to amplify the sound of the snottery gloop shifting around inside. My misophonia itched and I badly wanted to elbow him in the throat. But I needed this job. More than I needed a charge of GBH.

Paranoia kicked in as I pictured him standing behind me, staring into the back of my head. Maybe, I thought, he's stared at the back of lots of heads in the confines of a dark alley amid cries of pain, joy, and the vinegar stroke, gargling up at the moon, bathing in euphoric puddles of man gulch. *Stop it!*

The DVD ended and the lights flickered back on. I could hear a buzzing from the strip light above, and a soft tapping noise. I looked up and saw a moth fly repeatedly into the white glare, its small form jerking like a broken kite.

"I'd like to thank you, Ross," said Karl, moving to the front of the room again, "for listening to me rabbit on about safety. But at the end of the day we want you to go home to your family with the same number of fingers and toes you arrived with in the morning. Sign here." He pushed a piece of paper across the polished white surface of the table and handed me a Parker pen. I had a brief delusion of grandeur as I etched my John Hancock onto the dotted line.

I gave Karl his pen back. His hand lingered longer than it should have, long enough for me to notice the nail on his left pinky finger was filed and painted with black nail varnish. The letters 'c' and 'k' protruded from his sleeve, which obscured a fading tattoo. I imagined the letters 'd' and 'i' preceded them. I glanced up, and for the briefest of moments we made eye contact. I broke away first, and focused instead on his wet nose, glistening in the reflected light, a mountain of green gunge just waiting to give way.

Pain

Joy

Vinegar strrrroooaaaak ahhhhh!!

A fistful of knuckles rapped against the door and I jumped.

"That'll be the boss," said Karl. "He likes to give new recruits a wee booster chat to get them lit up about starting with the company. We're very lucky to have him. He's a bit of a Don Corleone in the world of metallurgy." He opened the door and let in a ripe, sweaty stench circulating around an end-of-bugle monstrosity.

"Ross the Doss! How's it goin', son?"

I felt a sharp pain between my ribs as the ten o'clock hooter signified morning break.

Dead Space Longannet

S TARING UPWARDS ON night shift is harsh and jagged because you can only just make out the roof. All dark grey and layered. You anticipate a slow death in the top dead space on level 198 with auld Murray spewing into your lug about how he would like to see you framed on his mantelpiece in a pristine white sailor's suit. A snapshot into the dark recesses of his perverted mind.

The tool shed buzzes with bodies and you notice the high bent railings warped and hanging like rotting fangs, inviting you to lean into the unbarriered gaps for an unplanned journey south and a twenty quid death levy. A half day token strike in your memory where the men would shout about the unsafe bastards cutting corners again.

You breathe in the black crystal shower. A constant falling of coal dust into your caked lungs. Lift doors open and shut with phantoms inside and rattle up the shafts to stop at invisible floors. You see the robots climbing into the morning storm to send dying stars into workers' faces with metal devouring machines. Fire klaxons are drowned out by the disintegrating sheets of steel.

The institutionalised storeman hands you a spoon and says, 'Go for it son … All the bacteria ye can eat … Feed like a king, ma boy … Asbestosis ye widny get in the best hotels … Be gid tay yer brother an' be his keeper or ah'll blade ye tay the big boss man.' And his booming rants blast over the thrum of the turbine hall and he rants and rants.

Then you climb, tool-laden, into the station lofts yourself. A blue collar drone feasting on an all-you-can-eat buffet of rat piss and pigeon shit. Up there with the night owls and their massive marble eyes and mad hoot hoot hootin'. Your job for the night in a dank corner of the penthouse roof and it's a fucking midden. The breeze from the Firth of Forth batters the slammer doors and sends up crab odours from the basement.

The horn from the Stevens' night van signifies chow down and a chorus erupts from salivating gubs. Are you ready, boys? Efter three. Wan, two, three …

Two rolls on sausage

Na na na

Two rolls on sausage

Na na na

Two rolls

Na na na na.

Rab the Stab

M ONDAY MORNING TRICKLED into my periphery courtesy of a reddish, oblong glow from the bottom of the dilapidated runner door. I could hear boots shuffling about like the feet of emperor penguins, as the head honcho laughed and snorted in his office like a kid after consuming copious amounts of Skittles.

Jammed like marshmallows into the van, the ten of us were shipped from the Graeme Hotel to a world of steel monoliths and paper mountains. BP. A prescription of back-stabbing, gutter snipes, confusion and brotherly love awaited us with open arms.

Aghast, I watched Rab the Stab cut his tomatoes with the same knife that had just cut its way through the hard, oily rubber attached to six heavy duty welding cables lying on the van's sodden floor. His chopping board for the now crud-stained tomatoes was an old copy of *Readers' Wives* that had seen more action than Andy McNab. He turned slightly, catching the light and allowing me to study the contours, grooves and cul-de-sacs of his massive moon-pussed face. If I looked closely enough, I would've found an old mess cabin in there somewhere, wedged solid.

I heard that Rab used to be a below-par goalkeeper for a pub team and every time he'd attempted a save, the ball had stuck square into his sniper's dream of a noggin. Clocking me gawking at him, he opened his mouth and it took a few seconds for the signal in his carbon steel brain to send speaking instructions to his lantern jaw.

"Good morning, you finely tuned tadger of a boy," he said, his face moving around like a bag of frogs in heat, his voice a Weegie-tinged crescendo peppered with his own brand of thuggish bravado. "Rab," I said, shaking my head in disgust, "is there a reason you're cutting the tomatoes with a knife housing enough germs to kill the entire population of Russia?"

"Yes, miniature nuts, there is," Rab replied. "I'm cutting my tomatoes in a ghastly fashion on a Monday morning in a van full of numpties, robots, and whipper-snappers who haven't even had a sniff of their Nat King because I'm Robert the Stab from Camelon. End of."

And just like that, the morning connection with Rab ended with him inhaling his two rolls on anthrax into his incinerator like a spanking new Dyson. Rumour has it that Rab was handy with the blade when he was a young gun, kicking around the Brockville club like a slasher with his Tam Shepherd plastic retractable joke knife.

I thought about a programme I'd seen on the telly the other week, where people from around the globe had this overwhelming desire to eat and digest inanimate objects like microwaves, TVs, bikes, doors and the odd double glazed window. I pictured Rab's wife standing in their flat in Camelon screaming, "Dae ye know how much that couch cost? An' you've gone an' ate the legs aff it, ya fat waster that ye are!" And then she runs out the flat crying, goes to lean on the railings but falls two storeys because Rab's munched them in a perverted hunger.

The fab shop roused me from my lethargy. Choruses of bullies hovered around the shop like gangs that plunged their way into working booths and young fragile minds. Fragmented wood-splints bounced from box feet as workers scarred young blood into adulthood; sparks flew from metal munchers and gave the drones a garish foreboding stance; buckled trestles blocked fire escapes, and outside the siren blasted across rooftops and spires to ingrain fear into a dog walker. Inhabitants jammed the wires. *Will she blow? Will she blow?* Cars are abandoned on the wet tar and people stare at the orange burnished sky's dragon-breath.

My head throbbed as I left my swivel chair and walked towards the stores to pick up my tools for the day. On the menu was a 24" stainless steel pipe repair that had to be completed ASAP, as the 40" pipeline that feeds the North Sea had been shut down at a loss of a million dollars per day. As I approached the stores, Rab the Stab's body language was leaning ever so slightly towards the 'sod off' variety, so I slowed my pace and produced a packet of Maynard's wine gums to cushion the impact. Everything in the stores came out of Rab's personal account and in turn belonged solely to him, so anyone asking for tools or equipment threatened the future of his family security.

"Here, Rab," I said, handing him the wine gums. "Have a couple of these bad boys to chew on. By the way, can I have a wire brush?"

"Nane."

I asked for a chipping hammer.

"Nane."

I asked for duct tape.

"Nane."

I asked for a galvanised bucket.

"Oh, wait a minute ... nane."

If he says nane again, I'm going to lose my fist into one of his face's deep gullies.

"Rab, do you actually have anything in this store?"

"I've got everything," he said.

"Give me a balaclava then."

"Nane."

The inner coward kicked in and I felt like I was sinking into the little puddle that had formed due to a hole in the corrugated roof.

Half five clock-out seemed like a shrine that I obsessively turned my attention towards. I returned to the fab shop empty-handed, cursing Rab's possessive hoarding.

Like a lukewarm shower flowing down a sun-drenched mountain, the gaffer approached and the holiest and most sacred music sang from his vocal chords, fine-tuned by the Buddha himself, to tell me that Jim Devlin had been seconded to the pipe job and I was to work with Scouse Wullie for the day in the heat of the shop. My eyes closed and I kissed a golden altar where Pamela Anderson was playing a harp, donning her infamous red swimsuit. Pink Floyd's 'Wish You Were Here' permeated from the tranny radio I kept in a box beneath my bench, so airborne factory dust didn't clog up its circuits, unlike Rab's brain. The loneliness of a long distance welder can be measured in coffee-stained books and an old battered piece of foam that gets dragged around metal containers in the hope of finding a corner of solitude.

As I clocked out that night, my heart was a slow purr, my body reprieved from the cold tension-sweats that usually cling to me after a ten hour shift in the chemical jungle. Navigating my way around the potholes in the car park, I thought about it never being resurfaced, left to erode to a sinkhole that would swallow the plant. The welfare of us minions just didn't seem important to the hierarchy.

On the way to my car I spotted The Hogg standing framed by the locker room door. He was smoking his infamous Cuban Havana snooker cue cigar and eyeing his

Harley-Davidson, which was parked about 50 feet from any other machine. The beast sparkled like a diamond on black satin and, when fired up, it breathed like a gang leader strutting into an enemy neighbourhood.

"Hogg-master!" I shouted. He looked up. "I see you're admiring your manhood extension," I said, grinning. "Twelve hours a day it spends in this bloody car park. You ever thought about taking a day off?"

The Hogg pushed himself from the cabin door and greeted me with the middle finger through a cloud of Cuban smog. "Some o' us hae a faimily tae bring up," he said. "An' whit's oan your agenda the night, numb-nuts? Lightin' the candles aroon the bath fur a romantic chugathon?"

"You're a poet, Mr Hogg, I'll give you that," I laughed. I walked over and gave my old verbal sparring partner a man hug. "But the bromance'll have to be put on ice till another day, buddy."

"Oi," he said. "Afore ye rush aff. Did ye hear aboot Rab yesterday mornin'?"

I shook my head.

"Well," said the Hogg, "when The Stab slunk aff tae the toilet efter mornin' break, Kelvin Conners slipped a crushed up Viagra intae his coffee."

Tears filled my laughing eyes. "That's mental, man, what happened?"

"The clown hud tae push hissel aroon the stores oan his runner chair so na'body wid see his boner, the poor nugget. Wee Stephanie kept poppin' in tae see him – an' ye know how much Rab fancies the pants aff her. His blood flow wid've been a ragin' torrent o' lust."

I could barely breathe. I had an image of Rab standing up and forming his own cricket wicket.

"An' then," The Hogg continued, "did ne no drap a piece o' paper, bend doon tae pick it up, an' poke hisself right in the peeper."

I lost it, falling to my knees and howling. When I'd composed myself, I stood up and wiped my eyes. I wrapped my arms around The Hogg one last time and squeezed. "Priceless. Laters, Mr Hogg."

I walked towards the Honda and climbed into the scent of old leather. As the engine shook into action, I got a main course of oil and petrol from the air con and was filled with a safe, homely feeling.

Idling over the rough, uneven gravel, I knew I wouldn't be back in this neck of the woods for a while. I was an industrial gypsy, a transient worker with itchy feet and a dwindling bank balance. It was time to earn some real holiday vouchers to exchange for freely-vended vitamin D.

Looking in my rear view mirror, I saw Rab the Stab standing, shaking his head beside his botch job of a Fiat Uno. The bonnet was up and smoke was belching from the engine. Just before my radio drowned out all external noises, I saw him tilt his head back and call the evening sun a 'BLOATED BASTARD!'. Before I got lost in the six o'clock traffic, I opened my lunch box, pulled out one of Rab's honking crud tomatoes and fired it into my starving gub.

Wise Old Owl

'How the fuck did Iain Banks create a world inside a bridge an' dae it sae masterfully?' Del thought, as he dipped his brush into the red paint and stared out over the kingdom.

He looked over the edge and imagined being dead before hitting the water. The papers had stopped documenting most of the jumpers because there were so many. The rail bridge seemed to be a favourite diving board for the end of life club. They would get off the train at Dalmeny and sneak along undetected, then start the long upwards climb until the terminal tilt and a final farewell to Edinburgh and Fife.

'Wit ye thinkin', Del?' spat an elderly voice from behind. Del turned to see Gilbert Crow standing a few feet away on the scaffold, a fag hanging from his crooked gub.

'Jist the usual shit, Gil, ye ken?' Del replied. 'How much money av no got, how long av no hud ma Nat King Cole, an' how long it wid take afore ye hit the water below if ye ever took the notion tay take a brave step aff intay the thinnest ay air.'

Gil screwed up his eyes and blew out a puff of yellow smoke that was instantly kidnapped by the wind; a constant this far up. 'Ah worry aboot you, Del, ah really do,' he said. 'Folks come fae aw o'er the world jist tae spend a few moments takin' in the spectacle ay Arrol's bridge, an' you're talkin' aboot how long it wid be afore ye hit the water. Deed that is, ya fuckin' numpty.'

'Listen, Gil, am no thinkin' ay jumpin', but loads ay punters must git these morbid thoughts noo and again, likes. Ah hink bein' this high up does hings tay yer heed, ken?'

Gil put his hands firmly on the handrails and inched slowly towards Del until his knee was touching his shoulder.

'Move o'er an' move yer paint tin,' he said.

'Wit fur auld yin?' said Del. 'Am tryin tay feenish this leg afore Hitler comes an' bags me fur yappin' tay you!'

Gil moved the paint and slowly slid in beside Del, putting an arm across his shoulder as if to steal some of his heat.

'Av been watchin' ye over the last few months, son, an' ye'v no been yersel,' he said.

Del was a little suspicious of Gil's voyeurism. 'Wit day ye mean ye'v been watchin' me, ya auld perv? Are you yin ay they predators thit linger aboot in online chat rooms?' He noticed Gil's hand and nicotine fingers, and wondered how many fags he'd eaten to do such a professional paint job on that skeletal skin. There must have been at least ten different shades of brown crud stacked up against his sabre-like fingernails.

Gil's eyes narrowed to slits. 'Av been aroon' a few years longer thin you, son, an' am no a bad judge ay character. How long huv us two been up here on nights, an' how many blethers huv we hud?'

Del smiled a little and leaned into his colleague. 'Must be close tay two an' a half thoosand blethers at least, auld yin.'

'Aye, it must be aroon' that figure,' croaked Gil. 'When two folk work the gither for as long as we've worked the gither, then a hink that qualifies yin hof ay oor partnership tay rise up above jist being his brother's keeper an' notice if somethin's wrong.'

Del grinned. 'Thanks fur yer concern, Gil, but am fine. Ah honestly am. Am a grown man, thirty years auld. Ah dinny need the world's auldest babysitter oan ma case!'

Gil laughed and pulled himself up to a standing position in three short, painful instalments. 'Auldest babysitter? Ya cheeky wee shite! Av got lunch boxes in the hoose aulder thin you!'

Gil idled over the scaffold planks towards the works canteen and looked back at Del. His young colleague was staring down through a gap in the boards at a passing tanker heading for the BP in Grangemouth.

'Am gon tay check the urn tay see if the water's boiled fur oor coffee,' Gil shouted, his voice battling against the howling gusts that swirled and roiled this high up.

Del didn't look up. 'Nay bother, Gil,' he shouted back. 'Jist mind an' check they mince pies on the lid in the broon bag.'

'Aye son, ah'll dae that,' replied Gil. 'Soon as av done a pish.'

Gil disappeared down the ladder and into the canteen. Del glanced up to make sure the coast was clear. Satisfied, he pulled out the letter from his trouser pocket and turned it over. It was still sealed. He looked back up towards the ladder.

'Wise old owl,' said Del out loud, safe in the knowledge that he wouldn't be heard. Then he lifted the envelope that held his goodbyes, ripped it into a million pieces, and sprinkled it down onto the welders crackling like brittle firewood below.

Clean Hit

H E FASTENED THE top two buttons on his duffel coat as a defence against the cold morning but the freeze had already set in. Lifting the cigar to his dry blue lips, he took a long pull and held in the smog for a moment, then slowly released it to the granite clouds. Reaching into his pocket, he pulled out the revolver, a companion for over thirty years and many an unknown's grim reaper.

He stepped from the kerb onto the main road, his mind racing from the white powder he'd just hoovered up his right nostril, a gentle nudge from some unknown ghosts in the Colombian jungle, slogging their futile lives away to keep him going. As he walked, he saw the morning sky reflected in puddles that had accumulated in the potholes and shook his head. He should be tucked up in bed neatly behind Sylvia, his darling wife of over thirty-five years. Sylvia, who was totally oblivious to his darker side; who knew him only as her darling Archie, a chargehand welder with Babcocks and Wilcox in Renfrew who spent most of his spare time with his model railway that took up the whole of the garage. In the underworld, Archie never had a name, just a calling card: a bullet hole.

Archie was on a contract. His last one, unbeknownst to his boss. One more pull of the trigger and the shooter was going into the smelter. Hitmen were supposed to be fearless and thorough, but the monster that was paranoia had started turning up at Archie's door a long time ago. Every clap of the knocker, every ring of the phone, sent Archie's heart over the furlongs. He hated this slowly growing conscience. The faces of his victims were starting to haunt his dreams; night dreams that had begun to leach into white knuckle days.

Falkirk High Street at half past four in the morning was peacefully desolate. It looked like the kind of dead end town you saw in old movies set in deadbeat middle America. Shops were boarded up and covered in weather-beaten fliers. Litter skipped over the cobbles like earthbound kites. The steeple – the famous steeple – rose like a rocket in the distance, majestic as ever, untouched by the scarcity infesting this once-vibrant street like poison ivy, giving the wind a hollow sound that chilled the soul.

Archie stepped from the High Street into an alley, stopping outside Armstrong's the barbers. He reached into his inside pocket and pulled out his old Samsung d500, a phone only two people knew about: him and his boss. It held a single text which he opened and read. Sweat formed on his brow as he glanced over the words, the light from the screen casting an eerie glow. He'd been given the green light to end another life and he knew he would do it, even if every part of him was screaming 'No!'.

His intended target was the bank manager of Lloyds TSB on Cow Wynd Corner, a stone's throw from where he stood. The details were bare, just time of arrival, type of vehicle, and the words 'clean hit'. What if this man had a family? What if he had grandkids that he got at weekends? It was Friday morning, quarter to five, and his victim would be here in thirty minutes. "Fucking man up, Archie," said the voice in his head. "What the fuck's wrong with you these days? You've turned into a right fucking shite-bag."

Archie pulled out his balaclava and slipped it on, the wool itching at his freshly shaved skin. "Just think, Archie boy ... one last dance ... thirty-five grand ... and it's all over. No more death games." He walked through the car park behind Howgate shopping centre, his hand tracing the outline of the gun concealed under the thick fabric of his coat. In the distance he heard business owners pushing up shutter doors as the aroma of freshly baked sausage rolls drifted over from Greggs.

Archie lifted his right arm and peeled back his leather glove to check the time. It was ten past five, five minutes till liberation. But the buzz wasn't there yet.

"Deep breaths, Archie boy. Think of the money. And it's a lot of fucking money." Archie pushed his conscience deep down, locking it away, and kept walking. Ahead of him was the darkened doorway that used to serve the old Burger King. Archie stepped into it and waited, counting down from three hundred in his head. He was still in the one-seventies when headlights flickered in the distance, beacon-bright in the pre-dawn dark. Archie tensed as a blue Mondeo estate trundled softly down the road towards him. This was the target.

The car pulled to a halt outside the bank's staff entrance. The driver sat still for what seemed like an eternity before finally opening the door. Archie watched him emerge and slowly pulled out his gun. This was it. He had him in his sights.

In all the years Archie had been erasing lives, this one felt the hardest. Something had to change. As the bank manager lifted his key to the lock and turned it, Archie swallowed hard and gently squeezed the trigger. In a heartbeat, it was over.

Archie walked to the rendezvous point to collect his money from his boss. He felt alive again. This was the most liberated he had felt in years. He walked past the high rise flats towards Callendar Park, his balaclava tucked neatly into his back pocket so as not to attract unwanted attention. He saw the bench at the side of the nine-hole golf course where a solitary figure sat. His boss was seventy-nine years old and looked like Mr Fredricksen from the movie *Up*. But beneath the old man's veneer of calm lay a barbarian. He was a cunning and feared gangster whose reputation spread like Saran gas.

Archie approached the bench and sat down. His boss pushed a brown leather briefcase towards him with his right foot, a routine they had both been through many times. The only difference was the location.

"Archibald." His boss always used Archie's full birth name, but Archie never complained about it. For good reason.

"Good morning, sir."

"Is the job done?"

"Of course, sir," replied Archie. "You know me. Clean hit. Every time."

The boss nodded. "The money's all there. No need to count it."

"Of course, sir," said Archie. He pulled out a silver duplex case. "Would you like to join me in celebration?"

"I might be an old bastard," said the boss, "but my ticker still feels thirty-five." He laughed, sounding to Archie like one of the old welding machines from work that only started on the tenth try.

Archie placed the silver case on his knee and opened the lid. He pulled out a mirror, a single gold bullet, and a rolled up twenty. Slowly twisting the tip of the bullet, he tipped the powder out onto the glacier surface, forming two short lines that resembled a pair of perfectly trimmed albino's eyebrows.

Archie handed his boss the twenty and held up the mirror. The old man hoovered up the first line and let Archie rattle back the second. The marching powder's effect was electric. Everything became crystalline and heightened.

"Holy fuck, Archibald. You never let me down."

The boss turned towards Archie and found himself staring down the barrel of a revolver. He never heard the silenced shot or saw the rising vapours. Archie watched his boss slump backwards and let a single tear trace the outline of his jaw. He grabbed the briefcase, glancing round quickly to see if anyone was near. Then he stood up and filtered into the trees.

When he got to his garage, Archie pushed the key into the rusted lock until it popped. He parted the timber doors and quickly stepped inside, closing them behind him. He pulled a cord to his left and the garage lit up. His whole body was tingling as the cocaine took hold. He walked to the back wall through a gauntlet of freshly spun webs and knelt down beside some loose gravel. He opened his toolbox and hauled out an old pair of rigger's gloves, pulling them on tight. A feeling of euphoria gripped his chest as he displaced the dirt to reveal a scaffold plank. He slid it to the side and placed the briefcase in the hole beneath. Beside eleven other cases. He covered the hole back up and spread the gravel evenly over the plank until it was hidden. Then he grabbed his work bag and emptied last night's lunch into the bin.

Sylvia greeted Archie as he walked up the stairs and into the kitchen.

"How did ye get on last night, darlin?" she said as she gave him a hug.

"Aye, no too bad, hen," Archie replied. "It wiz offy quiet, so ah managed tay feenish *The Girl On The Train*. Brilliant book hen, so it wiz."

"Oh, that's great, darling. An' Emily Blunt plays whit's her name in the film? The nosey alkie wumin who stares oot the carriage windy?"

"Her name's Rachel, hen. I hink Blunt's too gid lookin' tay play Rachel. Ah wid huv been happier wi Kathy Burke."

"Awe, she wiz gid in Larry Oldman's *Nil By Mouth*, so she wiz."

"Gary Oldman, hen, no Larry. Listen, am aff tay ma bed fur ma shift the night, awrite?"

"Okay love, but before yer bed did ye hear the news?"

"Naw. Whit happened, hen?"

"Some evil basturt shot the manager ay the TSB as he wiz gon intay his work this mornin'."

"Jesus Christ. Yer jokin', hen?"

"Am no, Archie. Check fur yersel."

"Okay hen, al pit the telly on up the stairs."

Archie never turned the TV on. He didn't need to. He felt safe because he always covered his tracks. He had it down to a fine art. He slipped into bed and set his alarm for 3pm, before reaching over and pulling down the blackout blind.

For the first time in a long time, Archie fell into a dreamless sleep. The next thing he heard was his alarm. His washing machine stomach was gone. He grinned as the smell of cooked bacon seeped upwards from the kitchen. He showered quickly, got himself dressed, then went downstairs for breakfast.

"Afternoon, hen," he said, giving Sylvia a peck on the cheek. "That smells braw." He leaned in and whispered in her ear. "Al give ye a smacker on the lips the night, hen. How does that sound?"

"Oooh, Archie. Stop that talk at this time ay the day," Sylvia laughed.

"Listen," said Archie. "Ah forgot tay tell ye that ma boss got paid aff last night."

"Awe, whit a shame, Archie. Whit a poor man."

"Aye hen, it's a shame right enough. There's a new boss in town, an' he starts the night."

"Well, let me ken how ye get on wi him, darling. Okay?"

"Will do, hen. See ye in the mornin'."

Archie picked up his bag that held the morning paper and his packed lunch and left the house. He walked up Oliver Road towards Falkirk High Station to catch a train that would take him into a world where he had no name.

Poverty Trap

'AN YET AGAIN the fridge is fuckin empty,' thought Deano as he stared stone-faced at the bare glass shelves. Admittedly, there was an onion in the vegetable compartment, but, like Deano, its best before date was long gone. It was seven o'clock on a Saturday night and he was already skint and on the bones of his arse. He'd only been paid on the Friday. In the space of twenty-four hours his full wage had been gobbled up by the debt machine. A karmic reminder of his impulsiveness. He felt like he was breathing in quicksand.

Still staring at the empty white space, Deano sat down at the table. It didn't matter that the fridge door hung open like an exposed lung: the whole fucking room was freezing. The wooden chair he was sitting on was like ice, and the white meter heater in the corner felt like someone had just painted it onto the wall, its pitiful buzzing like a mechanical wasp eating up all his electricity. Dean Comrie dragged his chair over to the heater, placed his blue hands on the serrated metal grill, and waited for his bones to defrost.

There was no putting it off. It was time for the long walk out to his mum and dad's in Tamfourhill, a small suburban shithole in Falkirk, to do his Oliver Twist routine. Reluctantly, Deano picked up the old Nokia that lay charging on the windowsill. He'd call his mum's mobile. He didn't want his dad answering the house phone. He asked too many questions. His mum was more compassionate. Less abrasive.

Deano pressed the green call button and listened to the incessant beeping. Or was that just his heartbeat?

'Hello son, how's it gon?'

Deano froze, suddenly choked up. He stuttered and stammered, struggling to make his vocal chords vibrate.

'Aye mam … eh … eh … kin ye hear me, mam?' Deano shivered. Even over at the heater there was no escaping the chilly blast from the open fridge door.

'Aye son, a said how's it gon?'

'Listen, mam, kin a come oot tay the hoose fur a wee blether an that?'

'Christ, Dean, of course ye kin. Ye dinny need tay ask tay come oot tay yer mam an dad's hoose. Christ!'

'Mam, dinny shout in case ma dad hears ye. A dinny want um askin questions, ye ken wit eez like.'

Deano got up and shut the fridge door, rushing back to the heater before his hands froze.

'Who's that yer on the phone tay, Barbara?' his dad chipped in from his recliner in the dinette.

'It's just oor Dean wanting tay come oot fur a blether, Billy. It's awrite!'

Deano felt his dad's under-the-breath laugh slice through his emotions like a surgeon's scalpel. He only needed to breathe a certain way to make Deano feel inadequate and invisible.

'Ye ken eez fuckin skint again an eez wantin fed,' William Comrie roared in the background.

'Billy, shut yer bloody mooth, will ye, an keep yer big whisky beek ooty this.'

Deano smiled to himself at the way his mum defended him. She was a beautiful wee hard-working woman who had slogged away her whole life in hot kitchens as a catering manageress. She had been retired ten years from Scottish

Power and couldn't shake off her role as the mother at the centre of the family. Everybody's rock. But push her too far and she bit like a rattlesnake. That was when it was time to vacate the premises.

'Are ye still there, Dean?'

'Aye, Mam, am still here,' said Deano. He rubbed at an eye. 'Dad's right, Mam, am skint again.'

'Awe son, but ye just got yer wage fi Morrisons on Friday. Huv ye spent it awready?'

The rumble from the number 9 bus that sat idling across the road poured into the mix of impending doom that stuck to Deano's chest like a suicide vest. Before he knew it, a stream of hot tears was rolling down his cheeks.

'A thought they paid mare money on night shift, son?' his mum asked.

Deano dried his face with the heel of his hand. 'They dae, Mam, but remember it's only Monday tay Saturday mornin, an it's only above the minimum wage. How am a supposed tay pay awe ma debts an feed masel as weel?'

'Listen son, cumon oo …'

'Dad's right, Mam. Am skint again an ma life's a pile of fuckin shite.'

'Noo Dean, stop this,' his mum soothed. 'Cumon oot tay the hoose an al make ye yer favourite brazed sausage. Yer dad disny mean wit he says. He jist worries aboot ye sometimes. He disny want ye tay make the same mistakes he did. He's aye sayin we should help ye set up a wee savins account an pit a tenner in it tay get ye startit.'

Deano lifted his head and looked out across the car park towards the municipal buildings. It had started to rain. For some reason the sound of rain had always propelled him into the past. So tonight, the sight of steam rising from the wet path outside the flat was enough to open up the portal into his childhood, where memories of Haggerston Castle and eight-berth caravans held far greater importance than empty fridges and dispassionate dads.

An image came into his head. Of a night in the caravan with his mum and dad and two sisters. The rain had started around eleven o'clock and had lashed down all night, so heavy on the aluminium roof that nobody else could get to sleep. But he'd managed it. He'd managed it because he'd let the white noise pull him into a secret place; a place he would kill to return to; a place that today was little more than a dream-filled battleground where his creditors rode around like the four horsemen of the apocalypse, hungry for his head.

'Whit do ye think, son?' Deano's mum's voice cut through the mental fog like a healing balm, lifting him from the rocks. 'Al send yer dad tay pick ye up in ten minutes an he'll drap ye aff later, okay? An he promises no tay say anything.'

'Aye Mam, nay bother, much appreciated. Yeez always dig me oot a hole.'

Deano ended the call and lifted his jacket from off the back of the chair. Fumbling in the pockets for his house key, he pulled out a pile of Tesco receipts. In amongst the squashed paper was a crumpled twenty pound note. Deano smiled in private gratitude as a sudden warmth spread across his chest. Outside, the number nine dropped into gear and pulled out into the night, splashing the pavement wet with fresh memories.

JOHN McKENZIE

Auld Polis

THE UNIFORM WAS hidden under his heavy black winter coat. The rules stated that you were not allowed to wear it in public if not on duty. Eddie Stewart disregarded this and many other rules that had been brought in since he joined the force, everybody knew him and knew what he was, so it was pointless keeping the coat on while inside; despite the cold. He took it off, hung it on a peg behind him and placed his hat on the bar. His black jumper was adorned with the newly designed Police Scotland logo. Its modern style looked out of place on him. Eddie was Auld Polis.

Only Shug and Jack were inside when he had walked in five minutes earlier, the lack of bodies in the pub meaning a chill from the dawn air had crept through the walls despite the heating being on. Laura sat next to an electric fire she had brought from home, her hands cradling a cup of tea to get as much warmth as possible into her body. She was due to finish in just over three hours at 8am.

The Ship Inn was next to what was once the entranceway to the town's redundant harbour but now served as the security gate to the still functioning glass works. The pub was almost three hundred years old and had always been a working man's pub, a place where you could get a drink no matter what time your shift finished. That tradition was still alive despite it not having an official twenty-four-hour license. As long as there was not any trouble, nobody checked what time the premises actually closed. Anybody who turned up wanting a pint always found the door open and somebody sitting at the bar. It was a place incomers to Alnock avoided drinking in due to its old and now undeserved reputation. It was a pub for drinkers; the men and women who sat beneath its low beamed ceiling led hard lives that required a reciprocity when they drank, and that included Eddie. He had been drinking there for most of his adult life and he had never seen any trouble worse than he would have encountered elsewhere. He knew from experience there were far worse places in the town.

On the still tobacco-stained walls, faces of former regulars hung in cheap frames. The tradition had started sometime in the late sixties and the wall had become a matter of pride to those in the pub. Some of the recent inductees had even chosen their photograph before they passed away. The Ship Inn felt like a community, perhaps the last real community left in Alnock, Eddie often thought. The men and women who filtered in and out at any given hour were known to each other. Some had family waiting at home but to many, the people they sat and drank with had become their real family. Over a glass, men shared everything; confessions, regrets and wrong turns always showed themselves when the glass was raised and defences were lowered.

'Same again darlin,' Eddie said as he placed the coins on the bar and headed through to take a piss.

The modern grey slate tiles that ran from the floor up the wall and covered the ceiling always took him by surprise. It was the only part of the pub that had been refurbished in the last twenty-five years. Parts of the bar had been painted and new seats installed but, overall, the pub still looked the same as when his sergeant brought him in for a lunchtime pint almost forty years ago. In the gents, instead of three cracked urinals, there was now a sleek and shiny chrome trough that ran the length of the wall, but Eddie walked to the cubicle and closed the door. It had started taking him longer to do a piss than he would have liked and now there was this pain that had appeared in his lower back. After only a few minutes, however, he had managed a small amount. Pleasantly surprised, he looked down into the basin and noticed that there was what looked like blood. He stood staring at it before deciding it must have been left over from the last person who didn't flush when he left. *Clarty bastard*, Eddie thought before zipping up and washing his hands in the sink.

His half pint and a nip were waiting for him when he walked back into the bar. There was a bit more heat in the place now and, as Eddie sat on his stool, the pain in his back subsided a little. Shug and Jack had finished their drinks and headed for home leaving only Laura and himself. Eddie caught his reflection in the mirror and saw that his face was flushed.

'I'm away oot for a fag,' Laura told him, wrapping her coat around her shoulders and leaving him alone.

'Mind an wrap up hen; it's fucking Baltic oot there this morning.'

'Aye well, cannie be any worse than it is in here.'

Eddie felt the cold air rush in, its harshness contaminating the meagre heat that had managed to build up. Nobody ever felt a rush of hot air, it was always the biting cold variety that invaded whatever warm place you found to shelter from the storm. He looked down at the bar. Seeing his hat sitting there reminded him again of the first time he came in with his sergeant, Bob Peterson. Bob was the type of polis that Eddie had wanted to be, firm but fair. He wondered what his old sergeant would have made of the job nowadays, of all the paperwork they had to fill in, all the new rules and regulations, and all the things they simply could not do anymore. Eddie thought Bob would hate it just as much as he did.

He remembered the incident with Davie Henderson not long before Bob retired. One or two drinks and Davie's temper mellowed, but anything more and he became unstable and violent and, more often than not, it was his wife Mary who was on the receiving end. It was reported to the station that Davie had been thrown out of the Tavern after starting two fights and breaking a window. It was also reported anonymously that Mary had been seen with a black eye. Officially, they could do nothing about the black eye as Mary had not reported it, and Bob and Eddie knew it would be a waste of time asking her about it. After driving around town for forty minutes, they eventually found Davie, picked him up and took him round the back to the car park for a word. As Davie lay on the ground heaving and crying, Bob bent down and whispered in his ear that if they ever saw Mary with so much as a hair out of place then he would come back, and this time it would be off duty. It was not until Bob's funeral that Eddie found out from Davie himself that Bob had helped him get off the drugs. He watched Davie walk down the line shaking hands with the family, breaking down on front of Bob's widow and telling her what a decent man her husband had been.

Eddie looked around the empty bar searching for ghosts but found nobody was with him. He looked over to the wall and saw the photograph of Bob. He wanted his police graduation picture there, not a picture from when he retired or anything with his family. He wanted to be remembered as Polis.

'You and me Bob,' Eddie said as he raised his glass, 'fuckin auld polis.'

Eddie checked his watch then, as he picked up his half pint to take a sip, he heard voices from outside. Laura was talking to somebody, but he could not make out who it was. The place went cold again; he started to feel a chill. The pain in his back wasn't helping, but the whisky should take care of that for a short time. He checked his watch once more and finished his beer. The bar felt that cold biting air enter again as the door opened and Laura walked in with Harry. Both shaking their shoulders and rubbing their hands together to try and get some warmth back.

'Can ah hae another nip when you've a minute hen?' Eddie asked as Laura made her way behind the bar, keeping her jacket over her shoulders.

'Fuck me, it's cauld out there,' Harry said as he stood next to Eddie. 'Maybe you better give me a nip as well to warm me up.'

Laura put two shots of Grouse into the whisky glasses, she did not ask if they wanted ice in them. Eddie handed over the money for the drinks.

'Cheers Eddie, your good health,' Harry said.

'Aye, nae bother.'

Eddie left his on the bar as he unhooked his coat off the peg and started to fasten himself up against the cold morning. 'I'll see yea later darlin,' he said to Laura as he went to pick up his drink.

'Tough shift?' Harry asked.

'I hope no,' Eddie said as he downed his whisky and picked up his hat. 'I've no fuckin started yet.'

The Park

A T TEN AM, the sky was a foreign blue. A kind of blue that you would find while sitting on a beach, gently dozing, trying to remember when you last applied the sun tan lotion. At your feet a paperback lay in the sand next to a glass, the dregs left untouched as they were too warm to be finished. It was that type of sky. Francis looked up and breathed deeply. It was some sky for ten am right enough, he thought.

There was not a cloud to be seen. Under such skies, the entire world had been given permission to feel good about themselves. He placed his coffee in the shade of the wall, leaned against the wooden bench and stretched out his arms, admiring the golden colour of his skin against the faded blue ink of his tattoos. His favourite was always the angel; it still impressed him every time it caught his eye. He remembered sitting down at the tattooist's looking at his arm. It had been freshly shaved and he realised it would be the last time he would see it naked. Billy, the tattooist, put the stencil on and asked him if he was ready. *Now there was a man living exactly the way he wanted*, Francis thought. Billy had an old-style pencil thin moustache and jet-black hair slicked back. It was cut in a way that did not hide the tattoo of the rose on his neck. He smoked roll ups and proudly displayed everything he loved in his life. Francis looked again at his arm, admiring the work Billy had done. His wife never liked it, she felt the angel was too scantily clad and showed too much leg to be angelic. Francis had joked that at least he would always have a woman on his arm. An empty smile spread across his face, vanishing as quickly as it arrived.

His coffee was still too hot to drink. Perhaps another five minutes and it would okay. He shouldn't have bought it as it was an indulgence he could not afford, but he felt it was important. It was a defiant fuck you to the bureaucracy of that place.

'Bastards,' he said out loud. Who were they to cast a judgemental eye over his life? Poring over every minute detail then deciding who he was and how he lived was not in line with their entitlements. Even the word 'entitled' was wrong. Nobody was entitled to anything in life, not really. Civility. That is what is missing now. His grandmother used to tell him that civility costs nothing, and he always tried to be civil to people. Even with those soulless shites in there. He picked up his coffee and blew on it, cooling it down before placing it back in the shade. The sun felt hot on his face and he could feel where his tears had dried. He was glad he held himself together, didn't let them see what they had reduced him to. He rubbed his hands over his face, feeling the last year of his life peel away. He cupped his hands around his face and let out a cry from a place so deep, he had not known it existed. Everything ceased.

Slowly, life began to return. He heard the birds singing, then a plane overhead and finally the small rumble of life continuing behind the trees. Francis opened his eyes and looked up at the cloudless sky. He was free. He was not entitled to anything from them. Neither, however, was he expected to give them anything of himself in return. He owed them nothing. In fact, he did not owe anybody anything of himself. He thought of that line from *The Prisoner*, 'I'm not a number. I am a free man!'

Calmly, he took in his surroundings for the first time. He saw the path where he used to walk his dog, always taking longer than was required so he could escape the house for a while. He saw his childhood, the wall he crashed into when his dad took him sledging and the two trees that he and his friends had used as goalposts. He felt himself smile from ear to ear. When was the last time that he did that? He felt grateful for the timely embrace of his memories. It was getting warmer. He undid his top button and slid off his tie. It was an ugly tie, a perfunctory present from his wife during the death throes of their marriage. Now that he thought about it, every tie he owned was ugly. They always choked him. Every day in that small office the noose got tighter and tighter around his neck, a noose that he had tied every morning. He got up off the bench, walked over to the bin and dropped the tie next to a collection of dog shit bags.

Feeling the sun on his neck, he sat back down and picked up the coffee; it still felt too hot on his tongue. He put it back down, content now that there was no rush. At the far end of the park, he watched George Gray walk through the gate with his dog. George was much younger than Francis but already an elder at the church that Francis used to attend with his wife. George was one of the Church of Scotland's chief accountants, the man responsible for God's money. Francis had always been fascinated by him. He thought George looked disappointed the he was not living in the 1950s, hiding his disgust at how the world was conducting itself. He was always neat and tidy, not a thing out of place on the man, and Francis could see this also applied to his dog as George held its lead tight in his hand.

'Morning Francis.'

'George.'

'I could not have picked a better fortnight to be off work,' George added. Francis wondered if he really meant that.

'Aye, it's a cracking morning to be alive.'

'I'm glad that Mary and I didn't book to go away. What a waste of money that would have been.'

Francis watched the dog sniff the grass around its owner's feet. George wore leather sandals with white socks and, in acknowledgment of the heat, chino shorts with a cream short-sleeved shirt. The shorts had almost military-style precision creases ironed into them. George had once told their minister at a coffee morning how much care and precision he took in getting the creases just so. Francis thought that everything looked out of place on the man, as if he wore casual clothes in protest. In the presence of George, Francis felt his shoes tighten and could feel the heat of the sun through the fabric of his heavy woollen black trousers.

'Day off?' George enquired, despite knowing Francis' situation.

'Last day,' Francis said.

'Last day?' George asked, slightly puzzled.

'It's hot today, isn't it?' Francis asked, ignoring George's own question. 'You know what I used to do in this park George? My grandmother used to take me here when I was a wee boy and I would walk around barefoot without a care in the world.

'Well …' George said, shifting uncomfortably from one foot to the other.

'It is a beautiful park,' Francis continued. 'We used to sit under that tree over there. I'd put my socks in my shoes then take off. I can still remember the feeling of the grass on my bare feet.' Francis looked around the park. It now existed both in memory and the moment. Francis saw George, standing while his own dog sat patiently for its master

'When was the last time you felt the grass under your feet George?'

He did not wait for a reply. He had dismissed George from his thoughts and did not notice him shaking his head in bewilderment as he continued his walk, the dog following at his heels after a quick pull on the lead. Instead, Francis reached down and slipped off his shoes without unfastening the laces. He then took off the plain black socks he had chosen with care that morning and rolled up his trousers to the knees. He unbuttoned his shirt sleeves, letting them hang loose around his wrists before picking up his coffee and tasting it; it was just right. Savouring the first mouthful, he started walking towards the grass, knowing that everything was exactly as it should be.

Death Throes of a Small Town

A faint outline of rooftops
Could be seen below the treeline.

The redundant chimney pots stretched out their necks,
Seeking a last gasp of air before final redundancy.

The woodland path allowed you to step
Outside the town. Beyond the confines of routine.

The importance of details lost to birdsong
Passion was reclaimed over the noise of impotence.

The wind carried her voice to me
The life I thought I knew lay buried in the mulch.

Men of the World

I

My father rested all his weight on the kitchen sink
Head bowed, shoulders hunched
The silver birch tree in our garden dominating
the window's horizon.
He listened respectfully to his father in law.
Bill, a retired prison officer
With a baritone voice and a barrel chest
Leaned in and spoke quietly.

I watched silently from the doorway
And could not hear what was said.

II

The day before your father died, I sat with him alone
In the hospice. His room felt tired, the paint faded
And peeling in the corners
An inoffensive white that was preparing to absorb
Another final breath without ceremony.

Not holding his hand and unable to risk
Looking him in the eye
I promised
I would look after his family. My family.

III

Her husband came home late
And went to bed with a stillborn silence
The orange glow of streetlight filled the room
Which he would forget whenever he thought of
that moment.
Instead, he would remember a choking darkness
As he sat up in bed and told her
He was leaving her for someone else.

His wife cried as he slept
Under their crisp white duvet.
The words spoken, his wedding vow severed
Their marriage bloodied like butcher's paper.

Tom Gillespie

Last Ferry to Ardrossan

DOUGLAS MACFARLANE PICKED up his phone, his keys, his briefcase and his packed lunch, kissed his wife on the cheek, and pulled the door firmly closed behind him, listening for the click. When he reached the gate, he stopped and glanced back at the house. His wife had moved from the hallway to the living room, and now appeared at the window, tapping her wrist and mouthing something about being late. He still hadn't managed to find the courage or decency to tell her. Avoiding eye contact and waving what only one of them knew was a final farewell, Douglas set off to catch his bus.

By the time he reached Central Station he was already exhausted, mulling over all the missed chances and bad decisions he'd made over the years. He checked the board and as usual his train was running late. Once again, he would miss the start of yet another pointless management meeting in which his boss would talk in fragments and impenetrable business-speak about his own vainglorious rise to the top. And, once again, Douglas would be reprimanded and threatened with disciplinary action for his insubordination or reckless disregard for his superiors. His demotion had been spectacular and now, finally at the bottom rung of the ladder, he had nowhere left to go but out. He was already on a final warning. Douglas figured anything could happen today, and probably would.

When the train finally pulled into the station, fifteen minutes late, Douglas trundled onto the nearest carriage and slumped down in a seat by the door. Glancing up the length of the train he spotted all the usual grey commuting corpses, garbling on their phones or stuffing breakfast baps into their faces. He looked out onto the platform. An elderly couple were wrestling with a bulging suitcase. He was shouting at her, and she was shifting it from hand to hand in frustration. For a fleeting moment, he thought about getting off to help them, but he was in no mood for kindness. He checked his watch and willed the train to start moving.

As the train approached Paisley, Douglas readied himself to join the queue of mordant zombies already heading towards the door, but as he stood up, the train lurched forwards and he was thrown into the aisle. An electric pulse of euphoric heat raced from his legs, through his chest, and set his heart pounding. At first, he thought he was having a heart attack. He'd suffered a minor one a few years ago and would recognise the signs and the accompanying coils of pain. This was very different.

When the train stopped and the zombies got off, Douglas stayed where he was on the floor. It felt satisfying to be beneath the surface, where he didn't have to put on a face for anyone. He didn't have to make excuses. The train doors closed again and Douglas stayed on the floor. The train pulled out of the station and Douglas still stayed on the floor, grinning triumphantly. In that moment of departure, he had finally made a choice to move outward and beyond what he could no longer control. He was free at last; free from his work, his tyrannical boss, and all of his desperately dull colleagues whose lives represented depressing facsimiles of his own. Free from the debt, the letters, the emails, the county court orders, the bailiffs. They were all narrowing and shrinking behind him as the train rattled on through the rain and the industrial dereliction of greater

Glasgow, winding slowly towards the fresh air of possibility. Still on the floor, Douglas stretched out his legs and, closing his eyes, focused on the reassuring rhythm of the rolling stock rattling along the old Victorian line.

By the time the train pulled into the last station, Douglas was back in his seat, fast asleep. The guard woke him with an impatient prod.

'Where are we?' Douglas asked, through the bleary fog of semi-consciousness.

'Ardrossan Ferry,' the guard said briskly, marching up the empty carriage to the front of the train and the end of his shift.

Douglas fumbled and stumbled down the aisle to the door still half-asleep, his belongings clutched under both arms. When he stepped off the train, the first thing he saw was a large sign swinging and squealing in the wind. Adjusting his eyes to the sudden light, the words came slowly into focus.

To the Ferries

The second thing Douglas saw was the guard he spoke with earlier, heading towards him.

'Are there any more trains?' Douglas asked, as the man approached.

The guard looked bemused and shook his head. 'This one's going back to Glasgow in an hour.'

'Anywhere else?'

'Arran,' the guard said with a smirk, 'but you'll need a boat for that.' And then he was off again, his eyes fixed on the vending machine at the end of the platform, his belly rumbling.

Douglas scanned the deserted station. There was nowhere to shelter from the wind coming in off the widening jaws of the Clyde, and the idea of hanging around for another hour in this purgatory, to then go back to the hell he'd just left behind, seemed too overwhelming to contemplate. Fishing his wallet from his coat, he counted what he had in the way of cash: four twenties and a ten. 'Hardly enough for a Reggie Perrin,' he thought. He quickly buttoned himself up and followed the path out of the station, looking for signs of life, or, at the very least, the ferry ticket office.

The tiny portacabin was located in the corner of a half-empty car park. Douglas stumbled in and shut the door behind him. Inside, it was surprisingly warm. A man in a vulgar tartan jacket was perched behind the counter, fiddling with his phone. He looked up as Douglas entered, his initial surprise slowly melting into a vacant professional smile.

'Good morning, sir,' he said, fumbling to conceal the phone beneath a pile of papers. 'It's a bit breezy out there today, eh?'

'When's the next ferry to Arran?' Douglas asked, ignoring the ticket agent's inane attempt at pre-loaded chit chat.

'Are you traveling by car or on foot, sir?'

'Just as I am,' said Douglas. 'Although I'm not planning on walking.'

'That's lovely. In that case you'll be able to catch the next one, which leaves in – ' The ticket agent glanced over his shoulder at a large clock on the rear wall. 'Oh, it's stopped,' he said with an embarrassed smile.

'It's twenty-five to ten,' Douglas informed him.

'Thank you, that's correct. The ferry leaves at quarter to, so that gives you at least another five minutes.' He leaned over the desk. 'If you don't mind a brisk walk?'

A wave of impatience washed over Douglas. 'How much is it?' For reasons he couldn't quite explain, not even to himself, he felt a need to keep moving. If he didn't, he'd surely slide all the way back into the rut of his former life.

'Single or return?'

The reply came almost without thinking.

'Single.'

'There's not much in it be honest,' coaxed the ticket agent, 'and you can always purchase your return at the other end.'

A blank stare from Douglas.

The ticket agent shrugged his shoulders. 'Suit yourself. That'll be £3.50.'

'Is that all?'

'I should have said thirty quid, shouldn't I?' the ticket agent snorted.

Douglas handed over a bruised tenner. The ticket agent pushed a few buttons and opened and closed the till a couple of times. 'Bloody thing,' he muttered under his breath. 'Sorry about this. I don't know how many times I've asked head office to get someone out to look at it.'

Douglas checked his watch again, and the till suddenly shot open with a loud ring.

'Business or pleasure?' the ticket agent asked as he counted out Douglas' change agonisingly slowly, coin by silver coin.

'Neither. Which way to the ferry?'

'Keep going straight on, follow the signs, you can't miss it. It's the big blue smoky thing in the harbour.' The ticket agent triumphantly finished counting out Douglas' change. 'Have a lovely holiday,' he beamed. Douglas ignored him and turned to the door, flipping his collar back up and bracing himself for the race against the wind to the quayside.

From a distance, the ferry looked pretty impressive with its large royal blue hull and tall, imposing funnels spewing out plumes of thick grey smoke in readiness for the voyage. But as Douglas approached, it seemed to lose its stature and morph into nothing more than an ugly metal box with a streak of the same vulgar tartan sported by the ticket agent running along the length of its side. Cars were filing into the rear entrance, and the lowered doors reminded Douglas of an overweight arse enjoying a colon inspection. The thought made him smile, but it was gone by the time he reached the gangway, where a small queue was forming, people huddling around their bags in an attempt to protect themselves from the wind. Douglas joined the line and slowly made his way up the slope. At the top, a crewman in regulation attire clipped his ticket.

'It's a wee bit choppy out there this morning, sir,' he said with a grimace. 'And watch your footing on deck, it has a tendency to be a bit slippy.'

Douglas boarded and followed his fellow travellers along a corridor and up onto the main deck. Leaning over the rail, he looked across the bleak Ardrossan harbour skyline towards the firth and the open sea, but the view was obscured by Lego blocks of containers and rusting cranes. Douglas' left leg shook with impatience. He checked his watch, then retreated back downstairs in search of the bar.

The Highland Snug was a tiny room tucked away at the back of the ship. With dark mahogany panelling and walls bedecked with dust-covered deer antlers and various species of stuffed fish, it looked more like a tableau from a bygone era than a tartan tourist trap.

'Good morning, sir,' welcomed the barman, his bevelled teeth and varnished lips forming the now familiar company smile. His tartan waistcoat and accompanying bow tie made him look like he was about to start a new frame at the Crucible.

Douglas threw his briefcase onto a chair near a corner table and peeled his coat off.

'What can I get you this morning, sir?'

Douglas flung his coat down on top of the briefcase and approached the bar. He scanned the pumps. 'I hear it's rough out there,' he said, not looking up.

'Aye, sir,' the barman replied. 'It was rollin' a bit on the way in.'

Douglas looked up and smiled. 'I'd better have a double then. Do you have any Macallan?'

The barman matched Douglas' smile. 'We do indeed, sir, and an excellent choice, if I may say so. Would you like ice with that?'

A broken crease formed along Douglas' forehead. 'Ice?' he asked in disbelief. 'No, but I'll have a half of your 80 Shilling.'

The barman nodded. 'Certainly, sir. Kill or cure, as they say. Sit down and I'll bring them over to you.'

'But it's just there,' Douglas said, pointing at the table, no more than three feet away.

The barman reached for a glass, the smile stapled to his face. 'It's no bother.'

Douglas retreated to the table and sat down. The barman wasn't far behind, carrying Douglas' drinks and a small bowl of nuts on a silver tray.

'There we go, sir. Cheers,' the barman said and quietly returned to cleaning the rows of glasses lined up along the counter. Douglas took a long slow sip of his whisky, savouring the first roar of peat-infused alcohol in the back of his throat. He closed his eyes, just as the ferry juddered and lurched to one side. Douglas' eye popped back open.

'That's us away,' said the barman.

Douglas felt the familiar rush of anxiety race through his chest again as the ferry moved slowly out of the harbour.

Opening his briefcase, Douglas removed the letter and, after a moment's pause, read through the contents again. There was no mention of the seventeen years of struggle and sacrifice to make payments in time, just a concise, cold, and clipped repossession order, alongside the date of sale by auction. Every day for over a year he'd promised himself he'd tell Sheila, and every day he'd failed. He'd secreted away letter after letter, snatching them up from the doormat before she saw them and keeping them bundled together in a locked drawer at work. They represented a collected catalogue, a diary of his deceit and growing despair. Their house was her home, the pride of her life, and the centre of her world. She knew nothing of the savage cuts in his wages and their spiralling debt. He'd always dealt with the domestic finances, and for a long time he'd managed, with some considerable skill, to fly innumerable kites. But since the crash and the imposed changes to his contract, the overheads had started to escalate and run away from him. At first, he contained it with new credit cards and overdraft extensions, as well as the usual debt consolidation numbers games, but it was like a runaway train, and the faster the debt accumulated the deeper he buried the problem. Before long, all his kites were grounded, all his options used up. He folded the letter in half, and then in half again, and slipped it into his inside coat pocket.

'Thanks,' he said to the barman, as he rose and left the bar, coat in one hand, briefcase in the other. The barman stopped drying the glasses and saluted Douglas' back.

It was blowing hard out on deck and Douglas had to grip the handrail to stay upright. The ferry was heaving from side to side, making slow progress through the swell and the spray. When he reached the front of the ferry, he leaned over the side and watched the waves break against the hull. Their motion made him queasy, and he had to look away, filling his lungs with deep breaths of fresh sea air until he felt better. Behind him, Ardrossan and the mainland receded slowly into the mist. He was moving forward, closer to the end of the line, and that seemed to be all that mattered. Everything else he would deal with when he was ready.

A teenage boy suddenly raced past Douglas and threw up loudly over the side. A thin, limp-shouldered man – presumably the boy's father – ran over and held the boy's arm, rubbing his back at the same time. If the aim was to relieve the boy's distress, it failed dismally. It only produced more vomit, and what could have been the boy's lower intestine for all Douglas knew. Douglas grimaced, more through memory than disgust. It was over five years since their own son had flown the nest to make his way in the world. His departure had left a gaping hole in both his and Sheila's lives that they'd found impossible to fill. Without the gravitational pull of their son's presence, they'd begun to drift apart. They existed together under the same roof, slept in the same bed, shared the same cooked meals every night, and stared at the same TV screen, but their internal worlds occupied such separate orbits they may as well have been alone. Their lives had become compartmentalised into blank versions of themselves that neither of them recognised or even liked any more. Sheila had her group of friends, her book club, her aerobics classes, and her nights out with the girls, while he worked, ate, and half slept until he had to do it all over again.

A gust of wind caught the boy in mid-puke and Douglas felt a light spray of vomit hit the side of his face. He stepped back, appalled. He needed something to wash it off with. God knows his hands wouldn't do. Where were the toilets on this thing?

Both sets of loos were packed with heaving, retching bodies splayed across sinks and hunched over toilet bowls on hands and knees. Douglas wiped his face with a gripped sleeve and turned back, following the signs to the restaurant, somewhere he thought was likely to be quiet, given the circumstances. Sure enough, the place was deserted. He approached the counter and surveyed the array of breakfast items laid out on hot plates: trays of sausages, bacon, fried and scrambled eggs, black and white puddings, fried bread, and a tower of toast stacked up to the top of the cabinet. Enough to feed an invading naval fleet.

'Coffee, please.'

The girl behind the counter looked more than a little surprised to see Douglas. Given the shenanigans out on deck, it's doubtful she expected to see anyone at all. She was short and young and looked a little out of her depth. She also sported the regulation snooker outfit for the national team.

'Would you like some breakfast with that?' she asked, almost apologetically. 'It's half price at the moment, for obvious reasons.'

Douglas smiled. 'No thanks, just the coffee.'

The girl took Douglas' money and handed over a large tar-black Americano. She smiled a wry smile.

'It'll be free in half an hour,' she said.

Douglas found a seat by the window and looked out at the battle-grey waves leapfrogging one another as though in competition. It was mesmerising. He had to break off after a couple of minutes for fear of being hypnotised. Returning to the here and now, he once more delved into his briefcase, this time taking out a notebook and pen. Turning to a new page, he held the nib over the paper. He searched his brain for the words that could explain everything; words that wouldn't cause Sheila any more pain than he'd already inflicted. He wanted to explain everything, why he'd lied and ran and left her behind, but the language wouldn't form and his hand stayed frozen over the barren white sheet. What could he say? It was all too late. He was a cunt and a coward. A loser. A liar. A failure. He wanted to say sorry, but it was all so hollow and empty and way too late. The house would be sold in three days. They were supposed to have vacated it over a month ago. Everything was broken and beyond repair. But then, as though inspired by the epidemic of seasickness that had overwhelmed the ship, words began to spew out of the pen, sprawling across the page like a panic-stricken worm. When he reached the bottom, he stopped and took a breath. He read the letter through, but the only word he could see was *sorry*. Tearing the page from the pad, he folded it in two, tucked it into his coat next to the letter from the bank, and finished his tepid coffee.

The ferry took forever to manoeuvre into Brodick harbour. And as the few cars and commercial vehicles onboard drove cautiously up the slipway, Douglas collected his things and made his way to the exit.

It was still blowing a gale outside, the weather, if anything, even colder than that left behind at Ardrossan. Douglas stumbled along the footway, still a little wobbly after an hour and a half of tilting decks and lop-sided horizons. He felt like a child, freed from vile parents but terrified of where he might end up. He scanned his new surroundings carefully, trying to work out which way he should go.

The village was small and pretty with buildings of various shapes and sizes scattered from one side of the bay to the other, all encircled within an expansive crescent of snow-crowned mountains that appeared to be pushing the human habitation towards the sea. There were beaches on either side of the harbour. To Douglas' left, the coast seemed to disappear into the next bay. To his right, the beach met a thick wooded area, leading to an isolated, rocky point. All of these choices. But which to take?

Before Douglas could make up his mind, he noticed a ferry employee – recognisable by the loudness of his Brig O' Doon single-breast jacket – hanging a hand-written sign on the noticeboard outside the ticket office. Douglas stopped to read what it said, but the sign kept flapping in the wind. Finally, the employee brought it under control and anchored it down to the wall.

'Is that right?' asked Douglas.

'Yes, sir,' the man replied. 'The weather is set to worsen over the next few hours, so the last ferry back to the mainland is at 12.30.'

'Lunchtime?'

'Correct, sir. It should have blown through by the morning, so we'll be up and running again tomorrow. Sorry about that,' he added, 'but we can't mess with Mother Nature.'

Douglas nodded and left the man to grapple with his sign. He followed the road out of the harbour and, when he reached the junction into the village, took a right along the beach road towards the headland.

Halfway to the headland, the road reached a bend and turned inland. Douglas cut across the grass verge and jumped down onto the beach, where he struggled across a few small dunes and piles of washed up seaweed, finally making it to the end of the bay and the edge of the woods. Spotting a stile, he climbed over and continued along a narrow pathway through the trees until he emerged out of the gloom on the other side into the barren expanse of the exposed headland.

Douglas tightened his grip on the collar of his coat and pushed into the wind, forcing his way towards the distant point. Clambering over some large boulders, he climbed up onto a large flat ledge and slowly inched his way along, battling to stay upright in the wind. At the edge, he leaned over as far as he could, his heart like a train in his chest. It was a sheer drop to the sea, thirty feet or more, with huge ferocious waves pounding the broken shore with relentless rage. Douglas stepped back, returning to the edge of the woods to escape the wind for a moment and to gather his thoughts. This was it. Here and now. The moment to move forward forever. He could turn tail and let the world tear him apart or he could depart in one piece and save the world the effort. Clarity returned, filling his lungs with cold, clear oxygen. 'Now,' he said softly to himself, and shifted his foot back onto the path.

Looking towards the village and then back out to the open sea, Douglas calculated that the tide and currents would be strong enough to carry him out of the bay and beyond. It seemed the perfect spot to disappear into the abyss and never be found. He took a couple of deep, shaky breaths, placed his briefcase on the path, and removed the letter to his wife from inside his coat. He placed the letter in his front coat pocket along with his house keys and phone. Then he gathered up some rocks, large enough to do the job but small enough to fit his pockets. When he was done, he returned to the rocky point.

This was the only way, he thought, climbing back up onto the clifftop. He was finally letting it all in and out, the failure and desertion. He would sink with his stones, but Sheila would go on. She would rebuild her life beyond him. He pressed forward, every muscle screaming, every thought compressing. His foot slid over the edge of the precipice. This was it. He leaned outward, forcing his body over. One more step. One more step.

Douglas' limbs refused to yield to the will of his mind.

'Fuck,' he shouted into the roaring sea.

He tried again, this time changing his position, hoping that gravity would drag him sideways and over. But again, his body refused to listen. His fear was controlling his movements like a puppet master, and his failure to fall was yet another humiliation and defeat. He needed some Dutch courage, a lot of it. Surely alcohol would help convince his nerves and muscles to play ball?

Emptying the rocks from his pockets, Douglas gathered up his things and retraced his steps through the woods, across the beach, and back to the village. By the time he reached the main street, he was all but done in. He spotted a hotel sign at the top end and staggered towards it.

A smartly dressed woman at the reception desk looked up when a bedraggled Douglas fell through the door.

'Oh dear, you look a bit blown away,' she said.

'Where's the – ?'

'First left,' the receptionist interrupted, anticipating the question.

The bar was half-full of locals and other similarly bedraggled travellers from the ferry.

Douglas approached the bar and emptied his pockets onto the counter.

'Double whisky and a pint of anything,' he barked to the landlord, who was engaged in a conversation with a small group of men at the far end of the bar.

'Be with you in a moment, sir,' the landlord replied, bristling a little at the interruption.

'Fuck's sake,' Douglas muttered under his breath. He found a seat in the corner by the door and slumped into it, leaning back against the wall and closing his eyes. To calm the galloping anxiety in his chest, he tried counting to a hundred. He'd got to forty-nine when –

'Sorry about that, sir. What can I get you?' Douglas slowly opened his eyes. The landlord was standing over him, smiling. Douglas stared at him for a second, trying to refocus his mind on the here and now.

'A pint and a whisky. A double.'

'Any in particular?'

'Ones with alcohol.'

The landlord nodded and returned to the bar. 'Were you on the ferry this morning, then?' he shouted over as he poured Douglas' beer.

Douglas nodded.

'A tad rough oot there,' offered the landlord, unnecessarily. 'Apparently it's set to get even worse later on.'

The weather didn't matter to Douglas. All that mattered was getting drunk enough to make it back to the point and over the edge. Maybe if the wind got worse he wouldn't need courage. It'd simply blow him over, rewarding Douglas with what he wanted most in this life: an end to it.

By the time the landlord had served the next customer, Douglas had already downed his beer and was holding up his empty glass for a refill.

'Bloody hell,' the landlord said, 'you're in a hurry. Are you here on holiday, or – ?'

Douglas didn't answer; just shook his glass by way of response.

The landlord took the glass from him. 'If you need somewhere to stay tonight, seeing as the ferry is off, we've still got a couple of rooms available.'

'No thanks,' said Douglas, starting in on his whisky.

The landlord shrugged and returned to the huddle of men at the corner or the bar, rejoining their animated conversation about the government's big plans for a new ferry terminal.

As the alcohol hit, Douglas could feel his eyes start to close again, but a tap on the shoulder pulled him back.

A small boy was standing by his table.

'Are you from Glasgow?' the boy asked.

Douglas tried to focus in on him. It wasn't easy.

'My Aunty May lives there,' the boy continued. 'We went at Christmas time. She bought me this.' He held up a small plastic action figure, fully equipped for battle.

Douglas struggled to find an appropriate response. Any response. 'Oh, right,' he said, barely managing even that.

'Bam! Bam!' the boy said, dropping the toy from the table onto the floor. 'Are you going to be staying here?'

Douglas shook his head.

'Bam! Bam!' the boy cried again, bouncing the toy off Douglas' shoulder and into his lap. Douglas handed it back to him.

'Tom,' the landlord shouted from the other side of the bar. 'You know you shouldn't be in here.'

The boy ran out of the bar, holding his toy aloft and pretending he was a rocket.

'Sorry about him,' the landlord said. 'My son's as daft as a brush, just like his mother.'

Just then all the lights went out and the bar fell into almost total darkness.

'Oh, Jesus Christ, no again,' groaned the landlord. 'That's the third time this week.'

'Aye, at least,' somebody chipped in from the dark.

The landlord clattered about behind the counter. 'Everybody please stay where you are. I'll have it back on in a couple of minutes.'

For a moment the bar was completely silent, anticipating an imminent return to normality. But nothing happened. Douglas heard a door open and caught a flash of torchlight. The landlord shot the beam across the room to his friends in the corner, and then straight at Douglas, who winced in its glare.

'Well, I think it's finally packed up,' declared the landlord, his voice disembodied and depressed. 'And I have no idea what we're going to do.'

'What about Eddie?' a voice called out. The landlord swung the torch beam over to its source.

'Fuck's sake, John, Eddie moved to London two years ago. Nab Noakes was the only electrician left, but he's away with the fairies with dementia. No, we are effectively a spark-less island.'

A collective groan from the darkness.

'Ah could gie it a go,' someone offered.

'I'd rather trust Dr Frankenstein with a fuse box than you, Roy,' the landlord sighed.

Another voice from the group at the bar piped up. 'Whit will ye dae wae aw yer guests, Frank? Thur gaun tae start moanin' pretty soon.' The landlord aimed his torch straight in the man's face.

'Thanks for that, Martin. That's really helpful.'

The door leading into the bar creaked open and a female voice broke the male monopoly. 'I can't believe this, Frank. I thought you'd fixed the bloody thing.'

The landlord cursed under his breath. Alison loved to point out his flaws. And he loved to defend them. It was probably what kept them together. 'I thought I had,' he said.

'Well, clearly not,' Alison continued, the pitch in her voice rising ever so slightly. 'You're bloody useless.' And with a loud huff and a slam of the invisible door, Alison left. A rumble of laughter rippled through the darkened bar.

Frank mentally counted to ten, then exhaled. Holding the beam to his face, which made him look surprisingly menacing, he addressed the bar. 'I'm sorry about this, folks. I don't suppose we have any electricians in the room who might know their way around a wiring system from the Edwardian era?'

Nobody spoke up. Douglas shifted in his chair. Frank turned his beam back onto him.

'Was that a yes?'

Douglas shook his head. He didn't want to get into this. After all, he was on the verge of leaving Planet Earth for good.

'Oh man, oh man,' Frank lamented, dropping his torch onto the counter and sending the narrow beam shooting across the room. More silence. Followed by more rumbles of muffled conversation.

'I could have a wee look at it, I suppose,' said Douglas, somehow unable to stop the words leaving his lips. 'Before I go.'

Frank picked the torch back up again. 'Are you a spark?'

'Could you at least not shine that thing in my face, please?'

'Sorry.'

'I'm a – or rather I was – a manager for an electrical engineering company, but I used to be a domestic electrician.'

'Halle-bloody-lujah,' exclaimed Frank.

'It's been over ten years, though,' cautioned Douglas, 'since I tackled any domestic wiring. I'm a pen pusher.'

'Perfect,' said Frank, ignoring Douglas' last remark. 'The system is at least that old, so it should be familiar to you. Would you mind havin' a wee look? I'll make it worth your while. You name it.'

'Jesus, Frank,' one of the locals piped up. 'Desperation makes you awfa generous.'

'I don't know if I can fix anything,' grumbled Douglas.

Frank shone his torch around the room. 'Well, there's only one way to find out. Follow the light. I'll take you through to the back.'

Douglas followed the landlord through to the back of the pub, and together they descended a narrow staircase into the cellar.

'Watch your feet on the stairs,' Frank said, guiding Douglas with his beam. 'They're bloody treacherous.' He threw the torchlight further ahead. 'The fuse box is at the far end.'

They had to negotiate their way around stacks of beer crates and awkwardly placed barrels, but they reached the back wall without incident. Frank opened a large box fixed a couple of inches off the floor. 'Here we are,' he said. 'It's been blowing for weeks, and every time we get some expensive company to come over from the mainland to try and fix it, it just seems to get worse.'

'I don't have my glasses with me,' Douglas said, peering into the gloom.

'Are they reading ones?'

'Aye.'

'Try these.' The landlord took his own glasses off and handed them to Douglas.

'Sorry, I'm Frank, by the way,' he said. 'Frank Price, the unfortunate owner of this broken establishment.'

Douglas shook Frank's offered hand and slipped the man's glasses on. Leaning over, he took a closer look inside the box. 'It's pretty old,' he said, squinting at the spaghetti junction of congealed wires and fuses.

'Can you see what it is?' asked Frank.

'Hold on.'

After some prodding and separating, Douglas spotted the problem. 'I think it might be your chiller cabinets. The cabling looks wrong.'

'We've just bought a new set,' Frank protested.

Douglas shook his head. 'It looks like they're running on six mil cable, but it should be thicker and on a separate fifty amp isolated switch, like your range cooker.' He scanned the rest of the board. 'To be honest, the whole system is hanging and probably not compliant.'

'Can you fix it though?' asked Frank. 'I mean, for now?'

Douglas rubbed his ear. 'It should be easy enough. We'll need to temporarily isolate your large fridges, but if we can do that we'll be able to get everything else back on.'

Frank's face lit up. 'Brilliant. Can you do that now?'

'Aye, I think so, but you'll lose your fridges.'

'Och, we can live wae that. I'll stick the white wine out in the coal house. It's caulder than a witch's tit-end oot there.'

Douglas lifted his glasses, rubbed his eye, then fixed the specs back in place. 'I'll give it a go, but seriously, the whole thing needs a complete rewire.'

'I know,' sighed Frank. 'It's a nightmare. But I'd be really grateful if you could just do a patch job for now. Just to get us through until we can get someone over from the mainland again.'

'Okay,' agreed Douglas. 'Have you got any pliers? Electrical ones if possible. I'll also need some cable cutters and a small screwdriver.'

Frank grinned. 'I'll go and dig oot ma toolbox.'

Alison had returned by the time Douglas and Frank climbed the cellar stairs back up to the kitchen.

'Alison,' Frank announced. 'Our saviour has arrived! This is – '

Frank's wife looked at Douglas.

'Well?' she said.

'Well what?' Douglas asked.

'What's your name?'

'Oh. It's Douglas.'

Frank hovered between the two of them.

'Douglas is an electrician.'

'Ex-electrician,' Douglas corrected.

'And he can fix our fuse box.'

Alison's frown turned into a warm smile.

'Jesus, Frank. Why didn't you say? That's fantastic, Douglas. I was starting to panic.'

'No problem,' said Douglas.

'We've got a full house tonight,' Alison continued. 'And an army of starving, stranded ferry passengers to feed.'

'May I?' Douglas indicated the large kitchen table. He sat down and started fiddling with the fuses he'd brought up from the cellar.

'I'll go get that toolbox,' said Frank.

After her husband left the room, Alison sat down next to Douglas. 'So,' she asked, 'what brings you to Arran?' She studied his expression as though she was reading every crack and line.

'I didn't get off the train at Paisley,' Douglas replied, not looking up.

Alison laughed. 'Can I get you a coffee, or – ?'

Douglas glanced up, confused.

'Don't worry,' said Alison. 'I can heat the water on the gas cooker.'

Douglas nodded in appreciation. There was a kindness to Alison's voice that made him want to cry. He hadn't experienced that level of kindness for a long, long time. There was something else too. A feeling he'd all but forgotten. The feeling of being wanted.

Frank returned before the water was boiled and slammed his toolbox on the table. 'Help yourself,' he said.

Douglas rummaged around until he found what he needed. A couple of fumbling minutes of fuse manipulation and he was done. 'Right,' he said. 'Let's try these.'

Back in the cellar, Douglas gingerly slotted in the first fuse. 'Fingers crossed,' urged Frank.

Nothing happened.

Douglas pulled it back out and switched it with the other rogue fuse.

Still nothing.

'Everything OK?' asked Frank nervously.

Douglas took a deep breath and pushed both fuses in hard with his thumbs.

'Hallelujah,' roared Frank, as the room lit up like a bonfire. 'Let there be light.' He peered up the stairs. 'Do you think it's on everywhere?'

Douglas checked the connections again. 'Should be.'

Frank slapped Douglas on the shoulder. 'Let's go see.'

As soon as they entered the newly-illuminated bar, Frank and Douglas were met with a wave of applause and cheering.

Frank pointed to Douglas. 'No me, he's the man.'

Douglas looked down at the floor.

Frank rubbed his hands. 'I can't thank you enough, Douglas. Can I get you a drink, and maybe a wee meal later? It's on us.'

Douglas shook his head. 'I'm fine,' he said.

Alison stepped forward. 'Or if you haven't got anywhere to stay, we could do you a nice room. I think we might have a couple left.'

'No, you're alright. Thank you.' Douglas was already looking around for his jacket.

'Are you sure?' asked Frank. 'It doesn't seem right. You've saved our bacon, quite literally, tonight.'

'It was no bother,' said Douglas, feeling increasingly uncomfortable. 'I've actually got to go. I'm late for a meeting.'

'The island is short of a spark,' said Alison, 'so there's always work to be had here.' Douglas wondered if she saw something in him that he'd failed to conceal. 'You're welcome back any time.' She wrapped her arms around Douglas and hugged him tight.

Douglas felt his emotions rising. He didn't want them to see him break down. Anything but that. He hurried out of the bar and down the hotel steps, aiming for the road through the village to the rocky point. But halfway there, he dropped down onto the beach again, sinking to his knees in the wet sand. He shivered in the cold air, half-frozen, barely aware that he was weeping. Weeping as though he'd lost a child. Or some other deep part of him. It was as though all the pain he'd held so tightly inside was now haemorrhaging out of him through a crater-sized hole in his chest. Frank and Alison had shown him kindness he hadn't experienced in years, and he was weeping for that. He was weeping for his fractured and broken life, and he was weeping for all the pain he'd inflicted on Sheila. But most of all, he was weeping for the person he'd once been.

Douglas cried out to the sea as the waves pounded the shore in retaliation. He railed against the world and what it had done to him, and what he'd done to himself. He let it all out: the rage, the pain, the fear, and the self-loathing. He loved his wife and he'd let her down. It was unforgivable. He was unforgivable. Sheila was the only light in the pit-black corners of wherever it was he'd been hiding himself. How could he treat her with such contempt and indignity? It was beyond reproach.

When he stopped, his voice cracked and hoarse from shouting, Douglas felt different. He felt light of head and thought, as though a lump of lead had been ripped from his skull. And yet still, inexplicably, he clambered to his feet and stumbled onwards towards the headland.

Approaching the edge of the cliff once more, Douglas reached into his coat pocket and removed the letter to his wife. He held it aloft, watching it flap wildly in the wind, desperate to escape his clenched fist. Gripping it with both hands, he tore it into tiny pieces and tossed them into the night. He did the same with the repossession letter. He popped open his briefcase, turned it upside down and emptied it over the cliff edge, shaking out the accumulated debris and dust of the dullest of working lives. And then, with renewed vigour, he jettisoned the leather albatross as hard as he could beyond the cliff and out towards the open sea.

'You can have that, but you're not having me,' he yelled, watching the briefcase drop into the depths of the dark. When he heard the distant splash, he stepped away from the ledge and stood for a moment in contemplation. He'd head back to the village. Take up Frank and Alison's offer of a bed for the night. Then ring Sheila in the morning and let her know he was safe. There were no guarantees he could make things right, or that the cliff-edge wouldn't beckon him again, but his chest felt lighter now, more buoyant, as though floating in saltwater. Surely that had to count for something.

As Douglas turned away from the wind, buttoning up his coat with fingers stiff from the cold, the crew of the Ardrossan ferry, fast asleep in digs less than a mile away, dreamt of clear skies and calm water, and a safe return to port.

Where Was I?

THAT'S WHERE AH wis but ah'm no there noo. Must be six months or mair. Keep up. Where the fuck's yer heed? Ah'm oot at Struthers an' Tipp noo, where big John works. Oh come on, ye know big John. John wae the dug wae wan ear. Whitshisname? The cunt that borrowed yer golf clubs an' never gied ye them back. Him. Anyway. It's no that bad up there. No a lot in it tae be honest. Ah'm oan wan o' they new flexitime contracts where they can gie ye the shunt whenever it suits them. Ah'm no that bothered. It's no like ah wis the fuckin' CEO at ma auld place, an' their pishy contract wasnae worth the shite it wis written wae. Who wur they kiddin wae their fuckin' package o' fuckin' benefits shite? The work's fine an' the team ah'm wae ur awright. An' at the end o' the day, a blocked shitter is a blocked shitter. Com si com sa.

So where huv ye been hidin' then? Huv ye been a naughty boy again? Mary said she saw ye in Asda wae anithir wummin. Ur you an' Carol oan the scrapper? If yis ur, yer in big trouble, young man. Ye'll be hard pushed tae land anyone else daft enough tae pit up wae your pish.

Did ah tell ye ah goat ma results back on Tuesday? The doacter says ah hufty cut doon on the smokes afore he'll refer me tae the hoaspital. It's anuff tae drive ye tae an early grave. He's pit me oan they stupit patches an' the gum, an' ah've boat wan o' they plug in peace pipes but ah canny work the fuckin' thing. Ah'll be fucked if ah let that stuck up overpaid ringpiece tell me whit a should an' shoudnae dae wae ma ain fuckin' lungs.

Still, needs must an' awe that.

That reminds me. If yer efter a bit o' cash there might be sum work goin' up at Struthers an' Tipp. Don't gie me that look. Ye don't need tae know anythin' aboot plumbin', they're always efter folk tae clean oot the tanks at their plant at Uddingston. If ye let me know where ye ur noo, ah kin pass oan yer details, if ye want me tae. Just gees a ring when ye get hame.

Raymond Plays the Puggies

RAYMOND WAS A strange character. He made his living playing the quiz machines in the pubs and socials around the city. He didn't have a shite job like the rest of us miserable sods. There was no need. You see, Raymond had the magic touch. You'd find him most nights playing the puggies with his pint on top of the machine and a roll up in his mush. Raymond was quiet, too quiet some folk might say, but he was a genius on those machines. When you were talking to him he would be alright for a minute but then, without a word, he'd be right back on the buttons.

'You okay, Ray?' I'd always ask him, because he looked so away with the fairies.

'Oh aye, nay probs. By the way, do you know whit the capital of Belize is?'

It was like Raymond lived and breathed those fucking machines. I wouldn't say he was an addict as such because you could argue it was quite an educational pursuit. It wasn't like he was on a couple of gallons of voddy a day, or feeding a serious crack habit. Raymond's drug of choice was general knowledge. And, unlike other forms of self-abuse, it was a lucrative dependency. Sometimes he was taking home up to 300 notes a week, tax free. You see, Raymond had a system; a method or an approach nobody could work out. He was a clever bugger n' all. He could answer any question you threw at him: *What is the specific heat capacity of mercury? Who directed The Guns of Navarone? When did Napoleon flee to Elba?* But it was more than just nous. I nearly found out his secret one night at the Vaults in Parkhead. Raymond had invited me to watch him win the £100 jackpot prize he'd had his eye on. After the last coin had rattled into the tray, Raymond said to me: 'Ah bet you'd like to know how I dae it?'

'Yer bloody right I do,' I said, anticipating a life of leisure.

'See that?' he said, pointing at his head. 'It's a camera.'

I wondered what the fuck he was on about.

'I'll say no more,' he said.

And that was that. It seemed that Raymond had the ability to remember every question he'd ever answered in every machine in every pub in Glasgow, and possibly further afield. It was an almighty and somewhat implausible task, but when I thought about it there could be no other way of doing it. That would explain why he was so quiet. He was working the system in his head.

The other strange thing about Raymond was his love of poetry. Every Thursday evening he would sit in on one of those writing workshops up at the university. We used to take the mince out of him something terrible, but we never put him off. He'd just shrug his shoulders, take a long draw on his roll up, and say:

'I just like the sound of the words.'

He never wrote any of the stuff himself, as far as I know, so like I say, a fucking strange guy. He took me one time. I think I must have been blootered. It was horrendous. It was like a gathering of perverts anonymous. Some wee raincoat merchant would stand up and confess all in rhyme and the others would applaud his depravity. But Raymond lapped it up. His face was beaming the whole evening. I think that was the only time I ever saw him smile.

Raymond was such a loner we just assumed he was on his tod. But one Saturday night we were all in the Griffin, tankin' it as usual, and in walks this vision of beauty. She was what my father would call a right Jacobs: long dark hair and legs up to her bum. I spotted her right away. First she went up to the bar and spoke to the landlord for a minute, and then she approached our table. I thought wee Shuggie was going to choke on his eighty shilling.

'Do any of you know where I can find Raymond Dorrell?' She had an unusual accent, kind of Spanish with the Scottish brogue mixed in.

'Who wants to know, doll?' Shug spluttered, always the first to make a tit of himself.

'I'm Celia, Raymond's wife.'

There was a deafening clatter of gobsmacked jaws hitting the floor. I couldn't believe it. How the hell did Rainman Ray get snagged up with her?

'Ray's not in tonight. You could try the Masonic Arms in Dundas Street. He's got his eye on the jackpot there I think.' I nodded, hoping that she might nod back, but she just about-turned and walked straight out. There must have been forty pairs of eyes watching that arse of hers manoeuvre majestically out the door.

And that was the last any of us saw of her. A couple of days later Raymond turned up at the flat, dead drunk. He staggered into the lounge and slumped down on the sofa. He was clearly in a bad way, and it took a while, but eventually I got the full story. It would appear that the night after her brief visit to the Griffin, Celia had left Raymond for her line manager at the Broo office. They were now shacked up together in his nice little semi in Giffnock. It seemed she'd had enough of Raymond's nocturnal vocation. Raymond ranted on about sorting them out and doing himself in. I did my best to console him and in the end he slipped into a drunken stupor. I laid him out and went to bed. I felt sorry for him, but I couldn't help thinking about those magnificent Spanish pins and the implausibility of their marriage. For one thing, Ray was an ugly bastard. More to the point, he'd never been what you would call an attentive husband. Christ knows, even I'd have been the dutiful husband if I'd been hitched to her. Anyway, it wasn't long after this particular bombshell that Raymond started to lose it big time.

For a wee while he appeared to be getting over his domestic catastrophe. He carried on as before, playing the machines and going to his poetry workshops. But I knew something was brewing. He was too quiet, even by his standards. For somebody who had just lost the most beautiful woman in Glasgow to a dole-snooping pen pusher, he was worryingly calm. And then it started. First it was an occasional wrong answer.

'I should have got that,' he'd say, sucking hard on his Golden Virginia. But before long, it had escalated into a full-blown disaster movie. Every answer he selected seemed to be wrong and the harder he pushed the further he fell. The system he had employed so successfully for years now started to work against him. It was like his brain had gone into some kind of meltdown. His descent was terrifying. Raymond was no longer in control of the game. He was losing money hand over fist and the strain was starting to show. Some nights you'd see him wandering about the pub hassling folk for change.

'Could ye lend us a quid, Tam?' he'd plead. 'Ah've just aboot cracked it the night.'

I stopped giving him any after a while. It was just feeding his dragon. Well, that and the fact he owed me about forty quid. For the next four months, Raymond must have lost thousands trying to regain his crown and his pride. Folk would try and avoid him when he came into the pub, or if they clocked him in the street they'd slide into the nearest shop. He had always been a bit of a scruffy bugger but now he was a total mess, and he reeked something terrible. I don't know how he managed to survive. We all tried to help him in our own way. Big Frank offered to take him to the doctor but he didn't like that idea much and had a go at smacking Frank in the gob for his cheek. And wee Shuggie, our local diplomat, told him he was hoachin' and suggested he nip down to the public showers in Central Station for a scrub. I tried to get through to him myself many times, but he was a man of few words was Raymond. It was like trying to communicate with a deep-fried Mars Bar. In the end, most of us just gave up. The only person that could help Raymond was the man himself and he was nowhere to be seen.

And then, without any warning, Raymond really did disappear. One minute he was there, stinking out the pub and tappin' money off some gullible punter at the bar, and the next he was gone. At first, I was a bit worried. I remembered what he'd said about topping himself. I thought about phoning the Great Western and the snorts, and I even went looking for him at his writing workshop. But he had done one good and proper. For a while, I kept an eye on the papers, half expecting to read some story about a body found in the Clyde. But then I figured that Raymond was too smart for suicide. He'd probably just got sick of us harassing him and buggered off somewhere else; somewhere he could start again.

'A career move,' I thought to myself. 'He's got on his bike and gone to find his form.'

That was about six months ago. Then, in March, I got a postcard. It was from Tenerife. One of those classy numbers with a picture of some bird with ice cream dribbling through her cleavage. It was from Raymond.

'You bastard,' I thought, as jealousy immediately got the better of me. 'Here's me worrying myself into an early grave and you're lapping up the sun in Espania.' Still, it was a relief to know he wasn't rotting in a ditch somewhere.

I read the inscription on the back. It said:

The camera never lies ...
All the best,
Raymond

'Good on you,' I thought. 'You got through it, ya jammy bastard.' I mentally wished him well and got myself ready for work.

And that was that. The last I heard, Raymond was playing the puggies in Las Vegas with a supermodel wife after winning big on Who Wants To Be A Millionaire. But it was wee Shuggie who told me that and I wouldn't trust his patter as far as I could shit gold.

The Camel of Castlemilk

M Y DAD HAD taken to reminiscing about his working days, when he ran a small landscape firm out at Bantone. Propping himself up at the kitchen table, he'd invite whoever would listen to sit down next to him. And like an old photograph album, he'd open out his memories and flick at the worn pages one by one. He never talked about the bad times, those dark days when Thatcher's ideological army systematically obliterated his business, along with the life he once lived. That was never his style. He preferred to dwell in the land of good humour, hope, and humanity.

Tonight was no exception. I found him in his usual spot with his dinner half-eaten and a whisky bottle half-drunk beside him. Leaning on his elbows and rubbing his hands together, a comfort habit of his for as long as I could remember, he was shaking his head and chuckling to himself.

'Tam', he said, when he spotted me coming in through the back door. 'Sit doon, fur Christ sake.'

I was about to decline his offer, but his laughter was too infectious to resist.

'What's funny?' I said, sitting down opposite him.

'Go get a glass.' He pushed the bottle towards me.

When I returned he was trying to swallow the dried out remains of what was once his dinner.

'Where's Mum?' I asked.

'In her scratcher.'

'Already? It's only half nine.'

'She's away ta ta wae the drink.'

'Have you two had a barney?'

'Och.' He waved his hand in front of my face like I was an irritating wasp. 'Hae a wee dram wae yer auld man,' he said, pouring himself an over-generous glug.

'Steady – '

'Och,' he repeated. And, pushing the plate to one side, he started sniggering again.

'What?'

'Ah'm no kiddin ye, sir.'

'Tell me.'

He let out a loud roar of laughter, coughing and spluttering whatever was left in his mouth out across the table.

'Dad!'

'Were you oan that joab wae the boys oot it Castlemilk?'

'Oh Jesus,' I said. 'You mean the garden job?' I worked for my dad in the summers and holidays, clearing debris and lifting stones from industrial wastelands, motorway embankments, and other godforsaken hellholes.

'That's the one,' he said through another choked laugh. 'That wiz some place, boy.'

He spread his arms across the table.

'Total nightmare,' I said. 'I think I did a runner in the end.'

'Don't blame you, son.' He took another large gulp of whisky.

I searched my jacket pocket for my cigarettes. 'Want one?' I asked, lighting up.

'Go on then,' he said. 'Yer mithir cleared me oot.' I helped him light up. Taking a long drag, he held it for a second then started spluttering again.

'Whit the fuck ur these?'

'Marlboros.'

'Jesus Christ. How dae ye like yer ribs?'

'Barbecued,' we both chirruped in unison. He took another toke and grimaced again.

'So what happened up there then, after I skedaddled?' I asked. 'I remember Big Ronnie getting chiselled on the first day.'

'Aye, some heed-the-baw planked him wae his ain shovel, then nicked it. Mind you, it wid be awfa hard tae miss his big useless dunderheed.'

My dad paused for a moment, staring at the table as though drilling holes in his mind for more precious metals. And then he was off again.

'It wiz supposed tae be a two week joab fur the coonsil, sortin oot the hoosin estate gairdens. Jesus Christ. Two weeks ma rectum. The coonsil were at it. They musta seen the wurd mug written acroas ma foreheed. We hud mair stuff pinched oan that joab than aw the ither joabs pit the gither. Spades, shovels, strimmers, you name it. If it wisnae nailed doon it'd be oot that door like greased lightnin.'

'Didn't the van get nicked?'

'Christ. Big Ron found it stripped oot in the next street. Even the ashtray goat liftit.'

'Remember the shop?' I asked.

'Oh Christ, aye – Stalag 59. An that poor wee Indian shopkeeper behind the counter.'

We started laughing again.

'"Some bampot's robbed the safe!"' he roared, with an accent closer to Cardiff than Calcutta.

'How the hell did they get in?' I interrupted. 'The place was like Fort Knox for fuck's sake. It was hard enough trying to get in to buy a paper, far less rob anything.'

'Ye wouldnae believe it, but the bastards dug a tunnel.' He let out another loud guffaw. 'A fuckin tunnel; aw the way fae the hoose acroas the road. It musta been sixty feet or mair. Like the fuckin Great Escape. Steve McQueen an his gang musta been months at it, diggin away wae nae bastard battin an eyelid. Ah mean, whit did they dae wae aw that bloody soil?'

'Dropped it oot through their troosers in the Asda car park?' I said, and we both laughed.

'The daft bastards,' said Dad. 'Aw the polis hid tae dae wiz follow the tunnel back tae thur hoose.' He feigned a military-style salute. 'Huv a good trip, lads – tae Barlinnie!' He took another puff of his fag. 'Mind you, they've probably tunnelled oot b' noo.' I choked on my drink and he smiled, happy to see me enjoying myself.

'An then there wiz that last street.' He paused for a moment, searching for the name. 'Braeburn Gairdens!' he said finally, with dramatic exaggeration.

'Oh bloody hell,' I said. 'I think that's when I bailed out.'

'The look on Big Ronnie's face when I telt him Braeburn wiz next on the list.'

'What happened there then?'

Dad locked eyes with me. This was a story that demanded all my attention. 'So me an the big ginger dunderheed knock on the first door in the street, tae let the tenant know we're aboot tae start on thur back gairden. The door opens an a wee dementit pensioner guy, aboot three foot nothin, greets us baith wae the end ae a sawn-aff shotgun, right in the pus.'

'No way! You never told me that.'

'"Fuck off oot ae it!" he hollers at us an he cocks the fuckin trigger. Big Ron looked like a man wae shite in his breeks. He says tae the wee nutjob, "Nae bother, pal", an wiz up the gairden path faster than a priest up a choirboys' cassock.' He shook his head. 'Jesus Christ, whit a place.' He started drawing lines on the table with his finger. 'Ah canny mind noo, but we must've plantit oot therty gairdins in Braeburn wae turf an wee trees, an ah'd say maist ae it wiz dug up an awa b' the end ae the day. Ah think even the coonsil goat fed up wae it an telt us no tae bother.'

'Did they pay you?'

'Aye, efter a few barneys. But we loast oot big time.'

Drawing heavily on the last of his cigarette, he let out another belly laugh.

'Ah've jist remembirt.'

'What?' I asked, anticipating a re-run of something he'd just said.

'Oh, Jesus Christ.' He leaned forward on his elbows again. 'Big Ron an wee Stevie were oan their last day up the dreaded Braeburn, an fur wance nothin hud bin nicked an naebody hud bin hospitalised. They wur workin at the back end a Braeburn, desperate tae git it aw done an git oot. When they arrived in the moarnin, late as usual, they parked the van up an Big Ron herd some shoutin an screamin fae up the road. They spottit a gang a wains divin aboot. They were aw runnnin roon an jabbin at a big lump a somethin in the road. So dunderheed an the silent wan goes tae huv a gander. An lo an behold …'

'What?'

'It wiz a bloody camel. Deed as a dodo, sprault oot fae wan side ae the street tae the ithir.' The tears were streaming down my dad's face as he fought to finish his story.

'No way.'

'Am tellin ye, sir. A bloody deed dormitory.' He patted his shoulder. 'Ye know, wae the two …'

'Humps?' I asked, shaking my head in disbelief.

'As God is ma witness. An it hid an empty boatil a Buckie stickin oot ae its goupin gub. Wan ae the wee toerags must a rammed it in there.'

'I'm not buyin this,' I smiled. 'And anyway, a dromedary's only got one hump.'

'Whit?' He looked at me as though in severe pain.

'A dromedary only has one,' I repeated, tapping my own shoulder.

Dad leaned in further until his face was almost touching mine.

'Tam, ah'm tellin ye. It wiz a great whoor ae a hairy beast, wae *two* humps.'

I sat back. 'So how the fuck did it end up there?'

Dad sat back too. 'Christ only knows. That's yer Braeburn Gairdens fur ye – a three ring bloody circus.' He wiped the tears from his eyes and snubbed the end of his cigarette with his fingers. 'Big Ron said it wiznae long afore the Braeburn elite turned up wae the fu butchers an a chainsaw. Stertit hackin it its erse.'

'Oh, come on.'

'Ah'm no jokin.' He paused to draw breath and force the words out. 'They wur supposedly floggin the meat in the pubs an passin it aff as T-bone … wae fur.'

He poured the remainder of the bottle into his glass and downed it in one. 'Right, it's goodnight fae him,' he said, slowly prising himself out of his chair. 'Ah'm aff tae ma baw baws. Ah hope tae Christ yer mithir disnae wake up.'

He stopped at the door, smiled, and said, to nobody in particular, 'Maybe the poor bugger ran oot a wattir.'

Shrapnel

H E WAS CALLED Albert but most folk knew him as Einstein. He acquired the name when he worked as a maths teacher at the old grammar school on Alexandria Parade. Apparently, he had a head for figures in more ways than one and those who knew him back then would say that he could charm the birds out of the trees. In fact, he was all set to tie the knot with some blonde bombshell from the Southside when Hitler intervened and turned Einstein's world inside out. When his call up papers came, he found himself in the Highland Light Infantry and was one of the first off the boat during the D-Day landings. On his way in to shore he took a direct hit in the head. The wound left him deaf in one ear and a few rungs short of the full ladder, if you know what I mean. They gave him a medal for stopping the enemy shell with his skull and every November he'd have it pinned to the lapel of his coat, the silver cross gleaming with polished pride as he marched through Dennistoun, shoulder to shoulder with his dwindling band of brothers. These days, Einstein was a familiar face on Duke Street. He was a quiet, polite man who had a smile for everyone; a gentleman, in the true sense of the word. He would often turn up at Cellino's Café with a flower for Mrs C. It was more of a weed really, but she was always flattered.

'Sit doon and have a cup of tea, Albert. Wid ye like a bacon butty?'

Einstein had a couple of jobs around Dennistoun. One was to help the bin men with the weekly refuse collection.

Every Tuesday, you'd see him following behind, picking up any stray rubbish that they'd missed. He'd gather it all together in his own bag and when it was full, he'd lob it into the lorry.

'Ah may be auld, but am no ready fur the van yet ye know.' The men would laugh, and the driver would give him a couple of quid. But his favourite job was at the local off-licence. Beveridge Brothers, or 'The Bevvy' as it was affectionately known, was a legend in Dennistoun. Next to Parkhead, it was probably the most important institution in the East End of Glasgow. It had been part of Duke Street life for nearly a century, and despite all the changes, makeovers and hullabaloo of recent years, the Bevvy had carried on as though nothing had happened. The shop was run by a cleek of middle-aged, permafrost-haired women in pale grey housecoats. They stood behind a large metal cage that enclosed the entire work area of the shop. After taking your order, then your cash, they'd reluctantly pass your purchase through a hole in the wire. All the alcohol was stacked up in boxes on the floor, gathering dust. Nothing was on display, except for a few handwritten, luminous signs advertising the week's special offers. Although the cage provided some degree of safety and protection, the Bevvy women were still able to intimidate and terrify all who staggered and stumbled into their domain.

Yet somehow, and with a great deal of persistence and inherent skill, Einstein had managed to charm his way into the hearts of the Bevvy women. Every night, just before closing time, he would appear at the back of the queue for the smokes and wait for Margaret to give him the nod. Then she'd spot him.

'Good evening Einstein, yer brush is in the office.'

She'd unlock the cage and, as he shuffled past the counter, the ladies would say hello and he'd smile graciously. Once inside, he'd remove his trench coat and start on the floor. First he'd sweep around the desk, the filing cabinets and the ledger books stacked up by the window, then under the small sink in the corner. Slowly, he would make his way out the back door and down the stone steps into the storeroom. He was very meticulous and thorough. To be honest, there wasn't a lot for him to sweep because the office was never used and most of the stock, along with the dirt, was piled up in the shop. But, 'if a job needs doin', it needs doin' right', he'd mutter to himself.

After about half an hour, he'd be finished and return to the shop. By that time, Amanda was pulling down the outside shutters and Margaret was doing the evening takings.

'By God, you're keen the night, Einstein. If ye like, there are a few boxes that need breaking up.'

'What was that?' He'd cock his good ear at her.

'Boxes, over there.'

'Righto, Mrs McFadden.'

At the end of his shift, Margaret would call him over.

'Thank you very much for all your help tonight, Einstein. There's a wee something for your hard work.'

He'd give Margaret a peck on the cheek, say cheerio to the others and pull the door behind him. Out on the street, the pubs would be emptying with the usual shenanigans in full swing. Einstein would hide the can under his coat and cross the road to avoid the bottles and the fists. Then he'd make his way back to the hostel.

In his room, he'd switch on his transistor and wait for the shipping forecast to start. Stretched out on the bare mattress, he'd sip slowly on his can, savouring every mouthful. Then at ten to one, he'd switch off the light and close his eyes. Perhaps it was the tune or the soothing lilt of the woman's voice, or images of frail wee sailing boats battling against the elements. Whatever it was, it worked every time.

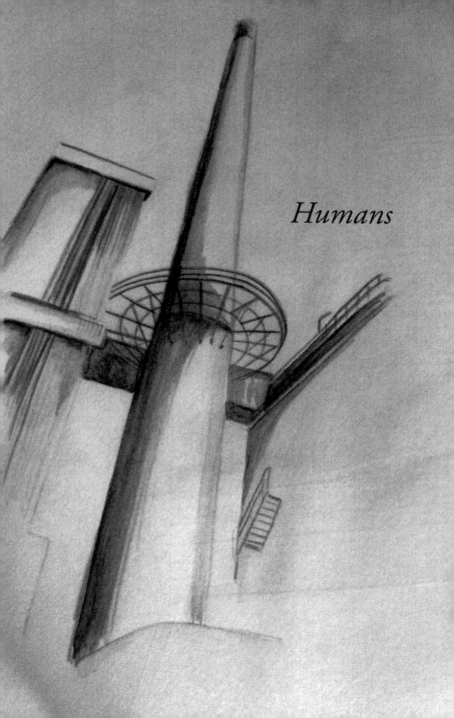

Humans

PAUL COWAN

Gull

A LIKE TAE go fur a wee donder. A ramble doon the toon tae ma wee coffee shoap tae sit in the corner nd gawk. A like tae coont the cars in the car park tae pass the time nd stare up it the sky. The windy seat fur some reasin is iywiz free. It's a gid gawkin seat. Hings happen ootside when a sit in thon seat. Last week when a wiz mid donder cumin doon the path towards the coffee shoap oan the wae tae ma windy seat a saw a seagul wae a buggered wing. Wan hoff ay mi wantit tae boot it oot the road but the ither hoff bent doon nd liftit it intae ma airms nd attemptit tae squawk its lingo. It first it tried tae brek free but efter five meenits ay me yappin in burd mode it stertit tae calm doon nd then it went deed still. Its wee burd napper slowly twistit roon till its wee beady een wur gawkin intae ma bigger marbly een. The baith ay us jist stood there oan the path nd gave each ither a right gid starin it. It wae its woondit wing nd me hodin it fur sum strange reasin. A cood feel its wee boney body pressin intae ma hons nd its alien een piercin right tae the back ay ma skull. Like it wiz transmitin some ancient wisdom intae ma psyche. Tellin mi no tae git too cumfy coz it hud been aroond since thon Big Bang. Fleein aroond in space tull this big rock ay oors formed nd gave it suhin tae land oan. A placed it oan the gress verge nd telt it tae flee up intae the sky efter it hud restit its wing sum mare. A reached doon nd dun sum reiki nd telt it tae be strong like Jonathan Livingston Seagull nd soar up abuv the cloods. Then a ran doon nd intae the coffee shoap nd ordered ma Americano nd sat doon it the windy seat which wiz empty is usual. A cood stull see it oor oan the verge nd it wiz starin north. Dain its mathematics afore its graceful leap fi terra firma. Up tae play wi the buffets nd gusts nd fleein chip pokes. Up where ma windy seat is the diamond shimmering below.

Strathcarron Hospice

the bounce from the wheels
I followed around in rotations
the red lights and

roadworks still pulsing in
a glass cabinet by
the sliding doors that asked you to donate

two lumps
lifted your feather frame from the
steel stretcher

onto your final bed
doves
were caged outside your room
where a bandaged hero

stood by his terminal door
holding his whisky like
an olympic torch and you remember

his vivid eyes as bloated suns
ready for
their journey to mars

and the hugs I remembered and
the tears I absorbed
and all the advice on life

choices and DIY and stretching
my mind beyond the
confines of a welding helmet

rose up like a shrine at the foot
of your bed as I willed
the pristine white sheets to

keep rising and falling, but they
finally fell and fell and rested
and you stood

on the hill beyond your room
and you were no longer bent and
crooked and sick

but tall and majestic and you
beamed like a lighthouse
beacon through a storm

and your darkness had gone
and the lights stopped flashing
and the road works

had ceased
and donations were made
and the wheels kept turning in

perfect rotations
and I remembered the day we found
a steel wire that threaded its

way through the woods by the broken
bridge and you whispered into
my ear, 'remember son, if

you ever get lost just shout
these words and I will
be there, look for me,

look for dad.'

Whispers in Angel

THE TATE & Lyle factory lay within the faded folds of the Greenwich skyline; a bricked crease; a map dot. Dark chatter hung in the air above it like a mushroom cloud, its fallout swooshing around radial drills and vending machines. Bodies clumped close, as though feeding into some communal beast. 'It's going to happen somewhere,' someone had said. 'And when it does, the claret will pour from every doorway as our city explodes.' You stand under an asbestos roof and stare into the radio speaker and wait. And you remember how that dark chatter polluted the air.

You recall young Shug telling you the phone signals were all dead, and everyone pulling out their handsets and punching at the screens to no avail. There's a silence as the radio glows in the corner and you start to hear those words you knew were coming and you close your eyes.

You visualise the underground line with its guttural thrum that sucks you into its diesel-tainted gusts and pushes you close to the line. Postures are crooked and bent and elbows connect with roaring jaws as knee-bones hug the tiled stairs. You sink deep down into the belly of Kings Cross St Pancras and you curse the subway. You hear electric man's bottle-top sliding up the distant fret board as he sings about a sunset in Waterloo.

Shoulders are jammed in electric doors that open and shut like dystopian Venus fly-traps.

You notice jittery geezers with the red eye glare sliding their hands, snake-like, into back pockets and bags, and your powerless shout is drowned out by the tannoy's ear-splitting boom. The tube stops at Tottenham Court Road and you think about werewolf corridors and a briefcase man getting shredded on the escalator. The shine from the tracks tells you the driverless cabin is coming to feast on the night. You wander lost in the Covent Garden bustle and dodge flying liquor and red flashing serrated steel. Northern Line sprinters hurtle towards Moorgate and sirens warble around the neon night above.

People fear people and rucksacks fly, and on a distant screen a man chants verse into a video camera and talks about an infidel; the first time you realise you were one. Bodies fly from a mangled bus that opens to the sky like a carnivorous maw. Russell Square becomes a funeral pyre with red twisted human shapes sliding down white walls. You walk head bowed along Trafalgar Road, magnetised by the whisky vapours escaping the Gipsy Moth's wheezing gut. South Greenwich is bathed in silence as black engines devour the white lined tarmac.

What's just happened below London? Tributes and tears pierce a hole through the veneers and you join the cry. It's finally happened. Double doors open onto a field of wreaths. No more veneers.

Wimbledon Common and Clapham Junction fade into an endless night and you can hear the whispers in Angel. Pale blue lips and beatless hearts. Doves paint the sky above the big city lights. Lost souls trapped in lanterns rise above heart-shaped hands and search for love and answers. You hear about false flags and your head implodes.

You see shadows on the path running parallel to the Thames as Big Ben's ritualistic gong swirls a haunting breeze through your bones. In its metallic din you hear the whispers of angels send the last train to Hammersmith trundling into the night.

Hungry for Love

I loved you my darling
I loved every part of your body
Those dazzling eyes
And crooked nose
Your shoulders
And brutish trapezius
Your unkempt hair like
Oiled hemp

Your meandering spine
Like the
Road to Damascus
Your captain's chest and
Corrugated abs
Your skin pulled tight by
Anvils
I loved you my darling

I loved your marble
Buttocks and hand-painted
Denim
Your long fat mojo
That filled every corner
And cracked
My ribs when erect
Legs that rooted into the earth
And rocks that shifted
Tectonic plates

You were the Hoover Dam
For my
Incessant
Incessantness
I just
Loved your bones my darling
My Vitruvian Man

I had you with basil
And mushrooms and a light
Sprinkling of ash
I boiled your skull white
As Samuel Barber's
Violins adaggioed
Around our
Last supper together
You were my
Lungs that breathed hope through
My mental fog

I smile from my heart as
Your skull sits
Perfectly sliced on
Our red
Cedar table
Two beautifully
Lacquered talismans

I told you you would
Always be a part of me
Our blood coursing
Through the
Same ventricles

I always
Get my way
My only lasting love
You were the one who snapped
Me out of sleep
My conscious awakening

I love you my darling.

Void

My dad left my mum with a gift
A terminal gift as he took
The long train
To the other side
Dropped into a hole with
His cancer
It had eaten him
From six foot five down to
Five foot seven
Deflated him over
His Zimmer
Like gnarled clothes
But he left my mum the most terminal of gifts
A blood and bone gift
For her to always keep close
Rooted into her soul like a
Cancer of the spirit
Clenching her
Voice into a fist
Twisting her spine helter skelter

Dismantling her presence
In intimate
Dehumanizing instalments
His corpse still
Dictating from his corner throne
In the living room
Disintegrated into the earth

Among the
Worms and lice
But still sitting there
A blue and broken shrine
Facing the television

He left her with something she
Couldn't see
A black hole in her
High rise flat
A wardrobe full of lifeless suits
And an unpaid bank loan
His empty cup
Collecting another layer of dust
On the kitchen table
Coated with another year
Three hundred
And sixty five year-long days to dwell
In her special gift
Freely passed on from her
Dead husband
Her the grieving widow

He left her with a void

Wull and The Gaff

A wiz sittin doon when a heard Big Wullie wiz deed
Wullie hud cord nummer seevin
It ma auld man's funeral
Gid cunt so he wiz
First met um
In a pub call The Gaff
Thit wiz nestled ahint the
Steeple in
The high street
A wiz aboot nine yer auld and a
Wiz fascinated
Wi gon up the toon and gittin
A hon shake
Nd a cola fi Big Wullie
Oan a Seturday moarnin
Eftur the karate

A ustay stoat
Up fawkurt high street wi ma
Karate suit oan
Nd ma polished
Broon brogue shoes
Ad ston ootside the pub door nd
Listen tay the din porin oot
The crack in the door
Then ad saunter in like a
Miniature Bruce Lee and git
Siroondit wi ma da's

Mates
Nd maist importintly
Big Wullie fi Westquarter
Ad tell um eez wig wiz slippin
Furrit nd eed
Pul it
Back intay place again
Naibdy
except us
Kent aboot oor wee joke

Ma auld man and Wullie wur
Best neeburs and they
Grew up the gither
In The Reddin
That wiz right nixt tay Westquarter
Wan day roon fi the Gaff they
Goat intay a scrap wi some
Guys fi Maddiston
Right ootside Kinoch's petshoap
They strolled intay the
Gaff efterwards wi bleck
Een nd burst mooths
And got
Nicknamed
The Pet Shoap Boys
Big Wullie wiz a constant presence
Awe through ma life
Until a goat
Told eed croacked it
A reached up nd pult back
Ma imaginary wig
Like oor wee

Joke wiz
Ingrained intay
Ma bones
Like marrow

"Here Jock there's that laddy ay
Yours stoatin up the high street wi
A bloody karate suit oan nd
Broon fuckin brogues," Big
Wullie's voice wid
Boom acroass the Gaff like the
Life blood ay the hale toon
Ma auld man wid look
Oot the pub windy and see ma wee
Napper booncin acroass
The cobbled stains
Oan the way tay the door
And eed shout
Tay Big Wull tay git me a cola
Nd ad ston in amongst awe
They giants nd
Hink a hud ma ain pint

A suddenly felt auld when a
Realised a wiz the same age noo
Thit Big Wull wiz whin a
Met um awe they years ago
Forty three year auld
A kent this coz a ustay ask awe
Ma da's mates how auld they wur
Coz they
Looked big and ancient
Wi rough hons

Nd big clumped wurk bits oan
In that moment as a sat in
The wee coffee shoap
Thit sits right nixt tay where the Gaff
Ustay be
A suddenly
Missed ma da nd Big Wull
A wished a could jist walk oot
The door nd look up and
See the Gaff sign
Above the padlocked doors
But thur
Wiz a new name
Up whaur it ustay be
But tay awe us nd the ancient
Giants thit wur noo floatin
Aboot in the cosmos
It will
iywiz be cauld the Gaff

JOHN MCKENZIE

1977

During a gap in our conversation
Cavatina played on the radio

that's from the Deer Hunter Dad said

the trivialities of what passed for closeness ceased
for that moment

do you know not one person moved after it finished
we just sat there, listening to that music

a sigh escaped and the declining wheeze of the clock
returned

everybody knew that a moment had passed between us

MasterChef

J IMMY BAIN WAS standing at the bar. His right foot was resting on the rail. His left hand holding the newly bought e-cigarette to help him cut out the Lambert & Butler. In swift neat movements he drew in the vapour and in a long, unsatisfied breath, blew the Frankenstein's monster of smoke up towards the television. Always taking neat measured sips. Never taking his eyes off the screen.

Jimmy was forty-one, divorced and living alone. The quiet that greeted him when he walked through his door accepted him as he was, and he had learned to appreciate that. It was a difficult transaction to make. He was used to the noise of the glassworks during the day and the sound of a home that was lived in at night. After his wife left, he dreaded going home. He would leave the radio on so there was at least some noise to greet him when he came in. His life was a simple, quiet one. Rising every weekday morning at five twenty-five, he showered, drank his coffee and walked to the factory. Five days a week, six am until six pm. Jimmy had started there when he was sixteen. Working on the production line at first then, after a few years he applied for and got a series of promotions. He was now a line manager and it was a job he took pride in.

He blew out another waft of vapour and kept his gaze on the television screen. There was no sound. He was watching *MasterChef*, which was on every night this week as it was getting near the final. As the judges stood pretending to show concern over the cooking time left for a contestant's shepherd's pie, Jimmy downed his pint and tipped the empty glass in the air to let Stephanie know that he wanted another. As she poured his drink, he separated the exact amount from the pile of coins.

Stephanie put the pint in front of him and picked up the coins. He took a sip of Tennents and then another deep draw on the e-cigarette. He still missed the Lambert & Butler that had been with him since he was fifteen years old. He went to put the remaining coins back in his pocket but noticed there was not enough for another drink. He would have to break the twenty in his wallet. He turned his attention back to the screen, thinking to himself that the shepherd's pie was fucked. Behind him, the door opened, and he felt the draft on the back of his legs.

'Evening James,' Ian said, heaving himself onto an empty bar stool.

'Aright.'

Stephanie had already started pouring a pint of Best and the two men watched the screen while waiting for Ian's pint to settle before being topped up.

'Christ that's been overdone has it no, looks like Izzy has had a go at it,' Ian said.

'Aye, fucking muppet put it in at the wrong temperature.'

'I cannae believe he got through fie last night, I thought he wis oot.'

Jimmy took his wallet from his back pocket. It had been a present from his wife and was over ten years old. Its brown leather was worn and creased. He took out a twenty and placed it on the bar. It was his round carried over from the night before.

'Cheers,' Ian said as he took his first drink of the evening and carefully placed the glass back on the mat with three quarters remaining. Both men watched the next contestant silently describe what his meal was going to be. They both recognised him from an episode the week before.

'Is that the boay that cooked the fish?'

'Aye,' Jimmy replied. 'Here I ran intae auld George at the work the day.'

'Auld George?'

'Aye, he minded me to ask yea aboot that hamer you're gonna dae for him.'

Ian was the same age as Jimmy. They grew up in the same street and went to the same school, Jimmy leaving to start in the glassworks and Ian to the council to become a joiner. Through the years the two of them had seen each other married, and in Ian and Izzy's case, have children. Both had seen the other through separation, although Ian had taken Izzy back. The affair was never discussed. Jimmy knew who the man was and suspected that Ian did too, but if he had to ignore that in order to share a bed with his wife then that was his decision.

'Oh, Christ aye, I'd forgotten aboot that,' Ian said

'Aye, that wis whit he thought tae.'

The two men laughed and continued to look up at the screen. The judges were now both standing behind a young blonde student, who was making what looked like a chocolate cake. Ian downed the last of his pint in two swift motions, 'Here, did she no make a dessert in the last round an aw?'

'Naw, mind it wis the other wee lassie that made a hash of the cheesecake.'

Ian looked at the screen again, trying to recall the other girl.

'Mind,' Jimmy said, 'she didnie leave enough time for the cream to settle.'

'Oh aye,' Ian replied as a smile came over his face 'the fuckn thing ran doon Greg's shirt.'

'Served the baldie old bastard right,' Jimmy said. 'Tennents and a Best when yer ready Stephanie.'

Jimmy's ten-pound note and change were still on the bar from the last round, but Ian placed a twenty of his own down in preparation for the drinks arriving. Jimmy picked up his tenner and put it in his wallet. As he did so, he remembered that George had handed him his phone number to pass on to Ian. He raked about in the front section, going through all the old receipts he should have thrown out a long time ago. He found the scrap of paper with the number scrawled on it. The drinks arrived as Jimmy sorted through his wallet, pulling out little bits and pieces from his past. There was now a small mound of paper next to his pint.

'Whits aw this?' Ian asked

'I'm just cleaning out the wallet.'

'Christ I'll hae another pint if yer doing that then.'

Ian laughed at his own joke and picked up his drink while returning his attention to the TV. Jimmy remained held by the scraps of paper in his hand. Most of the receipts were for books and albums he had bought, mostly for himself, but a few must have been for Ruth. After the separation, he threw out a lot of things and he did not recognise some of the titles. Looking at the receipts made him think of Ruth. The receipts were physical evidence of a life he used to have.

'Jesus,' Jimmy said to himself.

'Whits that Jim?'

Jimmy was holding a receipt from the restaurant that he and Ruth used to go to in the next town. It was over six years old but holding it in his hand it felt like he had just paid the bill.

'Cannie believe some of the shit that's in here,' Jimmy said, deflecting how uneasy he felt inside. He placed the receipt on the bar and reached for his pint, the need for a drink echoing how he felt the night Ruth told him she was moving out. His eyes were fixed on the wooden bar, he noticed every single one of its imperfections and dents. He did not see the smiles on the judges' faces when they tried the chocolate cake on the screen above.

'Fuck me that cake looks guid hen,' Ian told the screen. Ruth and Jimmy did not have any dessert that night; his initial shock had turned to an anger which he used to try and force his way out of the situation. Ruth remained silent, her hands resting on her lap and out of reach for Jimmy to take hold and plead with her; not that he would have done that. He folded the receipt carefully and put it back into his wallet.

'Whits that Ian?' Jimmy asked.

'Ahh yea missed it; yon lassie made a chocolate cake.'

Jimmy smiled. Ruth was not a baker. He could not remember her ever having baked a cake. She used to make a decent lentil soup, but that was all Jimmy could remember her cooking. Their dinners were always frozen or something from the takeaway, especially towards the end of their marriage. It had showed in both their waistlines. After the split however, Ruth flourished under the freedom that she had found, while Jimmy fell apart. Ruth started going to the gym with friends; Jimmy drank to excess with his.

Six months after the split and with his health and performance at work steadily worsening, he was told by his boss to see a doctor. Despite his initial protests, it was made clear that either he went and got help or he would be demoted back to the assembly line. The doctor signed him off for four weeks. It was enough of a shock to Jimmy.

He cut back on his drinking but did not stop it. Alcohol and going to the pub were part of who he was, part of the culture he had lived and breathed all his life. Instead, he moderated his drinking to a level that became acceptable to accommodate the life he wanted. It was not until he discovered that he had a passion for cooking that he began to feel comfortable with where life had put him. He had always read travel books and enjoyed the sections about foreign cuisines. During his forced absence from work, he started going through his old books and researching recipes on the internet. After a few initial attempts, he was surprised to find he was a natural cook. He bought more cookbooks, and over the next few months began to travel into the city to source more exotic ingredients. Cooking became his reason to enjoy being at home again.

The door of the pub opened again and in walked Harry with a tall blonde that neither Jimmy nor Ian recognised. Harry patted Jimmy on the back and politely nodded to Ian as he made his way towards the table in the corner. Jimmy raised his hand in reply as Ian shifted on his seat and quietly grunted a hello. The two men turned their attention back towards the screen, each distracting themselves from the past.

'You should go on that Jim.'

'Aye, so ye keep telling me.'

'Yon dinner ye made fur me and Izzy that night, ye'd pay guid money fur a meal like that.'

Jimmy finished his pint and watched the screen, he did not like to talk about his cooking. It was something he did for himself and did not usually share with others. He reluctantly had Ian and Izzy for dinner two months ago. Ian had asked as a favour. It was their first night out together since the split, and they wanted to go somewhere that they would not feel the eyes of the town on them. The gossiping that followed wherever they went only highlighted what had happened between them. Under the circumstances Jimmy felt he could not refuse.

Jimmy did not want to show off, but he wanted them to appreciate what they were eating. He knew himself that endless takeaways killed any sense of occasion. He decided to make them a steak; he remembered from the last time that they had went out that Ian liked his well done. Jimmy had spent the entire meal complaining that over-cooking killed any taste. "But that's the way I like it," was Ian's reply. Jimmy decided that, for Ian, he would cook the steak just enough for him not to complain that it was almost raw. Izzy was a problem; he did not know how she liked hers. He did not want to spoil the surprise for them, so he could not ask Ian. Ruth would know. He picked up the phone and called his wife.

It was the first time they had spoken in almost three years. He knew her voice but not the tone; she sounded happy. He found himself wishing he was making a meal that did not require him to ask anything of her. They exchanged pleasantries without delving much into each other's life, the right for both to do so had expired. Ruth said that she thought Izzy liked her steak medium rare. As he was about to put the phone down, he sensed Ruth hesitating before saying she wished him well and hoped that everyone enjoyed their evening.

'Aye, I can still taste that steak Jim,' Ian told him, 'you would dae far better than some o them that's been on it this year I can tell ye.'

Jimmy looked over and studied his friend. He saw that his hair was almost gone and what little he did have was almost white. The weight he had lost when Izzy left him was slowly starting to return. He remembered the night of the meal, Izzy looked radiant but humbled. She had fallen for a man who made her feel like Isabella rather than Izzy, before realising that he loved neither. Ian loved her as she was and that was enough. As he watched his friend taking a drink, Jimmy wondered how long it would be enough for.

'Aye well, at least you realised that well done is a fuckin crime,' Jimmy replied.

'Listen Jim, do you want another? There's something I need to tell ye.'

Jimmy looked at his glass, he still had half a pint left.

'An you think I need a full pint to hear it?' Jimmy said. 'Just tell me.'

'Hav yea spoken to Ruth?'

'No.'

Ian shifted in his seat and held his glass for support.

'Aye well, look Jim it was bound to happen sooner or later.'

Jimmy looked up at the screen, the man from earlier who had burnt the shepherd's pie was now attempting to cook a steak. Already, Jimmy could tell that it was not going well. He had applied too many flavours to the pan to spice up the dish. Steak was steak, Jimmy thought; it was a simple dish and did not need anything else added to improve it. Why don't these fuckin idiots realise that?

'Thing is,' Ian went on, 'Izzy asked me to tell ye that her and I are going tae Ruth's engagement party next month. You ken she wis seeing Shug Davidson?'

The sweat was now pouring from the contestant. He had spent too long trying to get the sauce right and had under-cooked the meat. 'Christ sake, look at the fuckin mess of that,' Jimmy shouted.

'Jimmy?' Ian asked, 'did you hear whit I said?'

Jimmy downed the rest of his pint and held the glass steady. He knew that Shug Davidson was a decent man, he could have no complaints about her choice. He put the glass down, picked up the scraps of paper next to his wallet, scrunched them up and threw them in the bin behind the bar. He nodded to Stephanie for another drink and took another puff from his e-cigarette. Blowing the cloud up towards the ceiling, he saw that the young woman was being congratulated by the judges. The credits started to roll.

'Aye,' Jimmy said quietly. 'I heard you.'

The Lie of the Land

By 8.30am the mist was retreating
To the banks of the Forth. Fragments of grey
Lingered between the border
Of town and farm, concealing the new gravel
Path and its perfectly trimmed hedge.

The morning held no sound.

Telegraph poles built with unnatural precision
Marched on the landscape, their black wires protected by
Bright yellow warnings of death
Adhered to by everyone but the crows.
They watched as the morning drew back
Its veil to reveal a widowed oak.
Stoic, in the middle of a recently ploughed field
Its leaves were still green
Despite cold October skies and butchered limbs.

Half a mile away, the looming outline
Of the town pleaded ignorance. Its church bells
Quiet, its smokeless chimneys ignorant of their past.
Its streets forgiven by the morning dew.

No 62

THERE WAS NO need to clean the window; the view would be as familiar to him as if he had taken the bus yesterday. Still, he used the sleeve of his jacket to wipe the condensation away. Small details were different. The town felt foreign. As the bus drove down the high street, he saw that Ramsey's newsagents was now a takeaway and the post office looked like it had been closed for some time. He wondered if the toys that used to gather dust on the shelf above the counter were still there, waiting to be sold behind the boarded-up windows. He noticed the dampness on his sleeve and a chill ran up his arm. Somebody pressed the bell and the bus stopped outside The Cairn pub. It still looked the same.

The sound of the bell brought a smile as he saw himself surrounded by his friends, all proudly wearing their Sixth Year blazers and finally taking their rightful place at the back of the bus.

He remembered Eddy pressing the bell continuously until the driver looked round and told him to *cut it oot*. His smile faded and his friends disappeared. Wiping his sleeve dry on his leg, he reached inside his jacket to take out the letter. It felt cold in his hand despite being next to his chest for the best part of twenty-four hours. He noted that his father's writing looked nothing liked his own. Sixth Year felt like it had happened to somebody else.

The next two stops go by without him taking any of it in. He was almost there, and could feel a tightening of his stomach. What would he say, what could he possibly say to any of them after twenty years? The bus pulled into a stop and the slow shuffling of feet followed. Looking up, he saw an old man flash his bus pass at the driver, blowing out the last remnants of his cigarette as he slowly made his way down the aisle. He thought the man carried a look of sadness, it seemed to cling to the fug around him. He turned his gaze back towards the window before feeling pressure on his knees as the old man heaved himself into the seat in front of him. The familiar scent of Lambert & Butler made the introduction for them both. He heard a voice but didn't hear the words. He turned from the window and said hello to his father.

Urn

In the living room of your last home
Your chair sat empty. The curtains
At 56 Elmbank had been kept closed
Your old blue ashtray
Remained on the fireplace unemptied
Half a dozen Silk Cut Ultras
Looking as if they had been stubbed out moments before.
The air lifeless, nobody had turned the heating on
Letters whose importance no longer mattered
Gathered at the foot of the door.
A white sheet had been thrown carelessly over your house.

I do not remember taking the clock from your mantlepiece.
For the past twenty years the clock
Has marked time in your absence.
It maintains shades of your soul that otherwise would
have been lost
To the purgatory of a charity shop shelf.
This clock has more meaning
Than the cold ashes buried under your headstone.

Midday, Friday

It is the last day of July
Two butterflies chase each other in the garden
Flying low over the carefully arranged
Beauty of next door's flowers.
White dances upon white
Green and red look to the skies
As their first petals fall
On our grey concrete.

I sit and watch, helpless with life.

The Retort

With perfect diction
A drunken Scotsman
Stood in the middle of the road
And shouted
"Aye, well at least I've got hair, yea pubescent wee shite."
Before heading back inside
To get out of the rain.

Routine

Each night as he took the dog
out into the garden before bed

He would watch her silhouette
Through the frosted glass

Of their bathroom window
Knowing that as she brushed every strand

Of her flame red hair
He had no choice but to fall in love.

TOM GILLESPIE

Soor Plooms

MARY MORETON SEARCHED her wardrobe for her best tweed two-piece and favourite silk scarf. She fixed her hair and carefully applied her makeup, making sure everything was as it should be. After a final cursory glance in the mirror, and a little smile to herself, she was ready to go. Today Mary was happy. Happy in her new home, which was a damn sight better than that awful place she lived in before, and happy she was meeting up with Jean, her best friend from secretarial college, already waiting for her in the lobby at the bottom of the stairs. As Mary approached, Jean looked up and smiled. The scent of rosewater and cinnamon hung in the air.

Mary tutted. 'Hod oan,' she said, and pulled a handkerchief from her handbag. She licked the corner and rubbed at a stain on the lapel of Jean's coat. Tomato soup? 'Yer a right slitter,' she said, cleaning Jean's clothes like she'd done so many times before. It didn't matter. Mary was just glad to be there for her, helping her through the worst of whatever this was. That's what friends were for, after all. She returned her handkerchief to her handbag, took Jean's arm, and led her through the wood-panelled lobby to the front door.

∾

'Mind yersel on they steps, Jean,' said Mary as they descended onto the driveway. Last night's weather forecast had been right: there *was* a definite chill in the air. The two women clung to each other for warmth as they slowly followed the line of trees down towards the gate. About halfway along, Jean stopped abruptly. 'Where are we going?' she mumbled, looking worried.

'We're catching the bus into town.' Mary rubbed her friend's arm and gently nudged her along. 'I'm taking you out for the day, remember?'

'That's awfa nice,' said Jean, tilting her head and smiling again.

∾

Mary closed the gate behind them and walked Jean over to the bus stop, lowering her gently onto the bench so as not to irritate her hip. An advertisement for Lipton's Tea peered teasingly down at them.

'There. That's nice, isn't it?' Mary said, squeezing in next to her friend.

They sat for a moment, two tired women, resting their aching limbs.

'I thought we'd start at the station café wae a wee cup a tea and one a they lovely custard slices.'

'That's awfa nice,' said Jean, her eyes shining.

'Then I thote we'd hae a wee walk through the park. It's aye sae lovely this time a year. And it's quicker that way tae the Roxy. I telt him we'd meet them both ootside at two o' clock.'

'Who's that?' asked Jean, looking worried again.

Mary leaned in. 'Your man and my man,' she said. Her closeness seemed to reassure Jean, and the silver-haired woman nodded in gratitude. 'That's awfa nice.'

Mary reached into her bag and found her poke of soor plooms. She took one and offered the poke to Jean, who rummaged around noisily before finally pulling one out and tucking it inside her coat pocket. From somewhere far away came the sound of a siren, rising and peaking and fading, replaced by birdsong and a light breeze. Meanwhile, Mary and Jean sat quietly, lost in themselves, enjoying being out.

∾

It felt like hours later when Jean giggled.

'What?' asked Mary, nudging her friend gently. Jean giggled again. It was soft and warm and infectious, and Mary couldn't resist joining in, even though she had to transfer her hard-boiled sweet to the other cheek to do so. These were the best days, when they barely even had to speak to enjoy the other's company.

The two women soon fell into silence again and watched as the world passed them by. A neatly-dressed lady with a small dog stopped to chat to them, gossiping about the siren they'd heard earlier and the price of butcher-meat, while her dog hungrily licked Jean's hand. When she finally left, Mary turned to Jean, her eyes wide.

'I think he might be about to ask me.'

'Oh, that's awfa nice,' said Jean, shifting around in her seat.

'I'm sure he's going to pop the question today.' Mary unwrapped another boiled sweet. 'It's his last day before he has to go back. If he doesn't do it now, we'll have to wait forever.' She rolled the sweet around in her mouth. 'Your Roy will make a lovely best man.'

Jean nodded.

'I know it's only been a few months,' said Mary, 'but he's definitely the one for me. He wrote me the most beautiful letter. Let me read it to you.' She searched her pockets and then rifled through her handbag. 'Oh, it must be in my other coat.' Sighing, she placed her handbag at her feet, rested her hands in her lap, and closed her eyes.

∾

'Good evening, ladies.'

Mary opened her eyes.

'Oh hello, er ...'

'Megan.' The woman wore a nurse's uniform and leaned over the bench so she could be heard. 'Did you have a lovely day out?'

'Aye, it was very pleasant indeed,' said Mary. 'John and Roy were hame oan leave, and we went tae the pictures.'

Megan turned to Jean.

'And did you enjoy it, Jean?'

Jean smiled and picked at the button of her coat.

It was Megan's fourth trip of the day. When she first started working at the home she was worried that letting the residents wander off to the old bus stop at the bottom of the drive would feel cruel. But when she saw the look of joy on their faces after a 'day out' she realised that their adventures provided great comfort to them. And now that the old road was closed to cars, it was perfectly safe. The only journeys the residents could take were through their past. A colleague had even managed to source an antique bus stop sign and original advertisements. It all added to the authenticity, and helped the residents find their way through the chaos and the fog to what little remained of their most precious moments. Mary and Jean were testament to the success of this rather unorthodox drug-free therapy. It had been two years since Megan had paired them up, and

Mary's proclivity for unpredictable aggression – triggered by a lifetime of spousal abuse – had now receded to a point where she could be trusted with Jean on her own, and no longer leave her battered and bruised after an afternoon together. To Megan it was both miraculous and beautiful that these lost and bewildered souls could find a little peace and contentment in the closing days of their lives.

Megan helped the elderly women to their feet and slowly walked them back up the driveway to the rest home. When they reached the bottom of the steps, Mary stopped. 'And I've some news,' she said, holding up her left hand. 'It's now official.' She turned her wrist from side to side and smiled.

'Oh, look at that beautiful ruby,' said Megan, taking Mary's hand and gently stroking her bare fingers, as she had done countless times before. 'That's stunning. Your man must be worth a bob or two.'

'We're gonny tie the knot as soon as it's awe oor.' Mary stuck her chin out defiantly. 'Nae point dilly-dallying aboot ony mair. This bloody war has caused enough trouble.'

'That's wonderful news,' said Megan. 'And about time too, eh, Jean?'

But Jean was standing to one side, her head bowed, mumbling softly to herself. Where she was, Megan could only guess at.

'Come on, then,' she said, taking both women by the arm and glancing at the sky. 'Let's get you two gallivanters in before the rain comes on.'

The Last Bus

By Christ it's cauld the night
Ur yae wait'n fur a numur wan?
Christ yool huv a wait
Wan jist past too minits ugo
It's fuckin cauld thow
The aulder yae get, the caulder it seems tay be
Ah reeli shoodnae be here yae no
The doactur telt mi no tae go oot it nite
When its sae cauld
It's the lumbago
Geez me awe kind a jip
Ah whit dae thay no oaniwaez
Whit ur ye ment tae day
Stay it hame way the wife an lissen i hur fuckin yelpin
No fuckin way, by the way
Ah wiz it the hoosin oafis the day
Thae fuck ye aboot sumhin terribul
Ye no ah wiz ment tay get the ful benifit
Un thar oanli geein mi hof
Yae no whit thay said tay may
Thay said ah widnae git oani mair
Oan account o ma hoos burnin doon
In thay think ah dun it
Theez cunts no nuthin by the way
Whit the fuck wid ah burn ma ain hoos doon fur
We wurnay evin inshoort
Tay think thit ah foat in a wor fur thay yung cunts
Tay sit ther in oarder me aboot
Ther awe fuckin ignirunt bastards by the way
Awe, therz yur bus noo son. Say hullo 'ae the wife fur mae

Polygamy

IT HAD BECOME something of a habit. Sheila would flake out after a long day at work and go to bed early, and I'd stay up late, chatting on social media and surfing the web. We stopped having sex a few months ago; I don't know why. We were getting on fine and I didn't think it was anything sinister. She probably just couldn't be arsed anymore. Life was hard enough without me huffin and puffin on top of her. I mean, we knew each other inside and out, so it was hardly fluttering hearts and the thrill of the unknown anymore. But I did find it difficult, missing out on the old heave ho. That's how it felt: like I was missing out. My job was wearing me down and, apart from the odd Friday night booze-up, I needed a little something or other to reduce my stress levels.

Like porn. But straight sex. Nothing weird or disturbing. You get to a certain age when you just need a kickstart, if you know what I mean. I had my favourite sites, ones that seemed to press the magic button. They helped me through, and for a while I was happy with that. But then, as the weeks passed, boredom set in and it never seemed quite enough. I found myself yawning my way through Dirk and Desiree going at it for the umpteenth time. And I was getting more and more distracted by the ads that kept popping up, often in mid-flight, obscuring my view: the women who lived within two or three miles of my house, gagging for a good time, no strings attached. At first I ignored them, but they wore me down after a while. And then one night curiosity finally got the better of me and I clicked the button.

It all seemed straightforward. It was a kind of dating agency with a difference. They guaranteed privacy and encrypted registration and promised to connect me with someone nearby. It sounded so simple. But it was still a big step to go from harmless fantasy to full blown reality. I'd never been unfaithful to Sheila before. It just wasn't in my DNA. A couple of friends had mucked their wives about, and when they told me about it, I let them have it. I'd always thought it was weak and cruel. But the more my mind wandered in and out of the idea, the more I convinced myself that this was not an affair or a betrayal. It was just a bit of harmless fun; a recreational poke for therapeutic purposes, like attending a yoga class or walking the dog on a Sunday morning. There were just more bodily fluids involved. So, after a day or two of resistance and further conscience-wrestling, I set up an anonymous email account and registered my details under the name 'John', a suitably neutral and common name that revealed nothing about my true identity. If I had any doubts, I thought, I'd just pull the plug and that would be the end of it.

A week went by and nothing happened. At first, I was checking my bogus account three or four times every night. But by the second week my enthusiasm had started to wane. And then it died completely. I all but forgot about 'John', my sexual alter-ago.

I was at work one day, about a month after signing up, when I took a rare squint at my account. To my surprise and shock, an email from the agency had landed in my mailbox. I waited until I was back home to read it.

After scanning down through a long preamble from the agency, I finally found the message at the bottom of the page. It was very brief, from a woman called Sadie. I assumed that was probably a made-up name like mine. My heart was thumping as I read her words. She wanted to meet up. I typed a response, a yes, and then a no, and then a yes again. And then, finally, I hit 'send' and waited for her reply. But nothing came back. Not that night nor the next. I'd almost given up hope when Sadie finally replied, days later, suggesting an initial meeting to see if we both wanted to go any further. I asked if she was willing to send me a photo. I needed to be sure her face would raise the flags and set the ships sailing, if you know what I mean. But she politely declined, saying she was worried about confidentiality and online security. Despite my reservations, I agreed and arranged to meet at a pub I vaguely knew, on the other side of the city, as far away as possible from familiar territory and people we knew.

On the day in question, I told Sheila I'd be working late, wining and dining some important new contractors we'd taken on. I was shitting kittens when I told her, trying not to say too much and give myself away, but she barely flinched. I hid a change of clothes in my work bag and breezed out with a cheery, 'Bye, love!'. I then spent most of the day clock-watching, until it became too much and I left the office early to get to my rendezvous in plenty of time.

It took me a while to find the pub. It was tucked away at the end of an alley in one of the most godforsaken corners of the city. The lounge bar was deserted, the barman looking up in fright when I walked in, as though he hadn't seen a customer in years. The place reeked of smoke and stale beer. The décor was circa 1974. I almost lost my nerve and legged it, but the call of the wild got the better of me. I ordered a pint and picked a table at the back, strategically placed to allow continuous observation of the entrance.

Two pints later, I was still alone, waiting for something I needed but was no longer sure I wanted anymore. The barman tried to engage me in conversation, but his patter was hopeless and I was in no mood for small talk. After a few failed attempts, he finally gave up and retreated back behind the bar. When I reached the end of my third pint, I'd had enough of waiting and was about to leave when the door juddered and then swung open. I couldn't believe it. It was Sheila. She was wrestling with her wet umbrella and still hadn't spotted me. Panicking, I scoured the bar for another exit, but it was too late. She clocked me sitting there looking guilty as hell. I forced a nervous smile, more to hide a galloping impulse to throw up than anything else. I felt like a safe-cracker caught before I'd even had a chance to get my tools out.

Sheila straightened her back and came over to the table. In a light, restrained voice she asked what I was doing there. From nowhere I heard myself spinning some yarn about how the works dinner had finished early and I'd stopped off for a quick pint before catching the late bus home. I thought she'd never buy it, but she just nodded and stood there shuffling her feet as though she wanted to leave. She mumbled something about meeting an old school friend for a drink but that it didn't look like they were coming. I asked if she wanted to have a drink with me instead. I thought if I didn't offer, she'd suspect something. I just hoped my date with destiny didn't turn up or I'd be well and truly fucked. To my relief, Sheila said she'd rather just go home. I quickly grabbed my coat and her arm and, with a final guilty glance at the front door, followed an unlikely sign to the beer garden, which turned out to be a concrete dumping ground for empty beer crates, overflowing bin bags, and cigarette butts. We weaved our way through the chaos and back out into the alley.

On the bus home, we sat in silence, listening to the secrets of other passengers but oblivious to our own. Back at the flat, Sheila made herself a hot milk and went to bed. When I heard her snoring, I went online and purged all my details from the agency's website, deleted my bogus email account, and cleared the browsing history on the computer.

Sheila and I never talked of that night again, but I remember in the days and weeks that followed, our relationship improved no end. Sheila seemed more attentive and happy and, to my surprise, I felt the same. It was as though my near miss with divorce, disgrace, and despair had rejuvenated our marriage; as though a dark cloud had suddenly passed over and we could enjoy each other's company again. And not only that, our love life was back on the boil, to the extent that I was having to fake a migraine or two just to get a good night's sleep and give my aching back a rest. I don't feel guilty anymore about what I did. I ventured close to the brink, but maybe I needed to do it to help me realise what I was about to throw away. Isn't it strange how life can sometimes spin on the hinge of a door?

Hum

AGNES DROPPED THE heavy bags of shopping by her feet and slumped, exhausted, at the kitchen table. She'd just walked a mile and a half. She'd have taken the bus if she'd trusted the timetable, or a taxi if she'd had the money. In the three months since Davie had left, the only thing she missed about him was his ability to carry the shopping in. Not that she was finding his leaving easy. After he'd gone, her life had fallen into chaos and despair. Virtually overnight, she'd lost her confidence and ability to deal with even the simplest of tasks. His betrayal and desertion had left her broken, penniless, and with next to zero self-worth. At her lowest point, she'd wanted to take a knife and run it across her throat; it seemed the only way to stem the torrent of pain rushing relentlessly from her heart to her head. But she couldn't find the courage, and her inability to end her own life became yet another measure of her perceived failure as a wife and partner. But as the days and weeks passed she seemed, somehow, to hold it together. Gradually, very gradually, she began taking the first tiny, faltering steps towards a life once remembered: a quick trip to the post box at the end of the road one day, a little further to the mini market at the corner of Duke Street the next. And yet, despite this reawakening, she still felt she was walking the wire; teetering on the edge of an ever-present oblivion.

Stretching her legs, Agnes noticed a long tear in her tights where she'd snagged them on the shopping trolley.

They were her last pair. She sighed and forced herself up off her chair. Coffee. She needed coffee.

Later, putting the shopping away, Agnes tried to focus her mind on what still needed doing: there were sheets and pillowcases to wash; the stairs to vacuum; her bank balance to check, on the off-chance there was any life left in her paltry overdraft. But then she stopped. Turned. Listened. Her worst fears were quickly confirmed. There was a noise, and it was getting louder. She'd first noticed it a few days after Davie had left, a strange low-pitched, persistent hum that seemed to reverberate around the house. She'd thought it was all in her head at first and put it down to her precarious mental state. But she could hear it in the kitchen, and in the hallway, and after a couple of weeks it was everywhere; in every room. She'd asked a neighbour to come round, but she couldn't hear anything. And there was a definite condescending tone to her voice when she suggested Agnes go get her ears syringed. Agnes had even considered ringing an electrician to check the plugs and the wiring, but she had no money to risk a wasted call-out fee.

Standing still for a moment, Agnes focused on the slow pulsating rhythm of the hum. Moving back out into the hall, she turned her head to try and distinguish its pitch from the background hiss of silence. It was coming from upstairs. As Agnes climbed, so the noise steadily increased. This was the loudest she'd ever heard it. She'd never been able to locate an exact source before, but now it was clear it was coming from the loft. At the top of the stairs, Agnes turned left and entered the bedroom. Her and Davie's bedroom. Where he used to – 'Stop it, Agnes,' she said to herself. 'Focus.' Dislodging bath towels and pillows, Agnes hauled a pair of dusty step ladders from out the back of the airing cupboard. Crossing to the door, she tripped over something sticking out from under the bed, and half fell to her knees.

'Fuck,' she yelled, as her shin rapped painfully against the bed frame. She dropped the ladder and sat on the edge of the bed, rubbing at the bruise through another tear in her tights. 'What am I doing?' she said aloud. 'I'm 52, not 22.'

Glancing down, Agnes saw what it was that had tripped her up. It was one of Davie's work shoes, a great carbuncle of a steel toecap sticking out from between two bed boxes. She imagined him at work, hobbling about, trying to play down his predicament without showing what a complete shite he'd been to her. 'You really are a total arse, Davie,' Agnes said, giving the shoe a hard, life-affirming kick. It skittered awkwardly across the carpet and tumbled down the stairs. Agnes picked the ladder back up and returned to the task at hand.

Positioning the ladder below the loft hatch, and making sure it was stable, she began to climb. Halfway up, she felt wobbly and stopped for a second to compose herself before carrying on. Even before she unlocked the hatch she could tell the hum was significantly louder than before, and she could now detect slight changes in its tone. Agnes slid back the bolt and cautiously opened the hatch. Inside, it was pitch black, but the humming was now deafening and seemed to be coming from the far corner. Climbing further into the roof space, Agnes felt for the light switch. As she fumbled, something flew past her face, almost knocking her backwards through the hatch. It happened again, a loud buzz in her left ear this time. She quickly located the switch and flicked it on. It took a moment or two for her eyes to adjust to the glare of the bare bulb, but when they did, she gasped.

Something was moving in the corner. At first, she thought it was a person hunched up in what appeared to be a long grey coat. The closer she peered though, the more it became apparent that the thing wasn't human. Whatever it was, it was attached to the roof and wrapped around one of the support beams. And it was definitely moving. Despite her fear, she began to crawl towards it to get a better view. As she approached, the hum intensified and the rhythm increased. It was when she was within three or four feet of the thing that she finally saw them: a huge clump of insects flowing like tar from a small hole in the side of the structure. It was an enormous bees' nest. Panicking, she quickly retreated back through the hatch and down the ladder.

She spent the rest of the afternoon pacing around the kitchen, fretting over the bees and what to do about them. She could call the council, but it was Saturday. Or she could go back to her neighbour and see if her useless husband would know what to do. But in the end she just couldn't face another cold and tortuous conversation. Finally, she gave up and crossed to the fridge, trying to focus her mind on dinner. Like it or not, she had to eat.

Later that night, after a couple of feeble nibbles on a sandwich and half a bottle of Aldi's own brand Lambrusco, Agnes' thoughts returned to the unwanted visitors in her loft, and curiosity finally got the better of her. 'Fuck it,' she thought. Downing another large glass, she went back upstairs to get the ladders.

Standing on the landing, staring up at the hatch, Agnes fought to overcome her fear. 'I don't need you, Davie,' she whispered into the dark. 'Not anymore.' Agnes took a deep breath and began to climb. She slid the bolt back slowly, so as not to make too much noise, and then opened the hatch, inch by quiet inch. Reaching inside, she found the light switch and flicked it on. The nest was silent and still, with nothing flying in or out. Agnes climbed into the loft space and inched closer, trying to see what was happening. As she leaned in towards the nest, a large bulge appeared in the side and a swarm of bees exploded out. Agnes tried to scrabble back but she couldn't make the hatch in time, and in an instant they were all over her, attaching themselves to her like demented limpets. She flailed her arms at her tiny assailants, but the more she resisted the more animated and determined they became. In seconds, her shoulders, face and hair were completely covered.

Agnes' instinct was to fight back and shake them off, but that wasn't working. If anything, it was making the situation worse. 'Calm down,' a voice deep inside her told her. 'Calm down and everything will be okay.' Agnes stopped moving and slowed her breathing, as the bees continued to surge out of the nest and push themselves into the thick black mass forming on and around her. There were now so many bees on Agnes' face, she feared she wouldn't be able to breathe, but somehow they seemed to avoid her airways. She could feel the weight of the swarm pressing down on her arms and chest. Still, she hadn't been stung, and the bees now seemed less agitated. The buzzing and pulsating slowed, and for a brief moment ceased altogether. And then, slowly, the collective mass began to swing gently from side to side, the bees working together to synchronise their movements. And as their strange dance spread down her waist and legs, Agnes too began to sway in a slow, hypnotic waltz, moving backwards and forwards in harmony with the rhythm of the bees' wings, as they swooned and caressed her limbs. And with the rise and fall of the waves, Agnes could feel her strength grow, every nerve resonating and sparkling with electrostatic joy. She was, at last, awake and vital. She stretched out her arms to allow each individual bee to embrace her. And then, miraculously, they seemed to draw her body upwards. She felt her limbs stretch, her feet rise, and now she was levitating above the boards, a few inches at first, and then higher, until the top of her head brushed against a roof beam. It was as though the bees had passed all of their collective energy into her and she had become one with the swarm. They had crowned her their new queen. She was their leader and their saviour. And in that moment of devotion, unasked and unprompted, the bees gave Agnes a reason to keep breathing; to stay alive and to carry on.

The Waltz of the Clocks

'USUAL,' SAID JAMES, propping himself up at the bar. The landlord, drying a pint glass, greeted him with a familiar nod.

'How's tricks this evening?'

'Usual,' replied James with a smile. He eased his copy of *The Racing Post* from his coat pocket and scanned the form. The landlord placed a small whisky on the mat in front of him. 'It's been dead in here all week. Nobody seems to want to drag themselves away from their televisions these days.'

'Christ knows why.' James took his first sip and grimaced as the sting of alcohol hit the back of his throat. 'There's bugger all on at the best of times.'

'How you keeping now?' the landlord asked, leaning on the bar for a moment.

'No too bad. The hip's still giving me hell, especially with that nip in the air.'

'My father had chronic arthritis, amongst other things, but it was the drink that got him in the end.'

'The devil's work,' said James, taking another sip.

The landlord laughed and returned to cleaning the row of glasses lined up behind the till.

James searched his pockets for his pen and mulled over his options. He circled a couple of horses in tomorrow's 3.30 at Haydock: Pretty Lady at 8-1 and Hello Sucker at 20-1. He liked to place wildcard bets; just a quid or two here and there. Sometimes it paid and sometimes it didn't, but it was more exciting than sticking with the favourites. He glanced up. The landlord was clearing out one of the pumps and it was making an unearthly sound. James smiled to himself and carried on scanning the paper.

The large grandfather clock in the far corner of the room let out a loud chime. 8pm. He'd been engrossed in his paper for nearly an hour. The landlord had bought the clock in an auction a few years ago, but it had been too big and cumbersome to lumber up the four flights of stairs to his flat. So it now found itself wedged up against the back wall, its dark mahogany frame looming ominously over the patrons and reminding them of the proximity of last orders and turfing out time. Yet, despite its imposing and rather austere appearance, James liked it. He found the repetitive thump of the brass pendulum familiar and reassuring. And every hour, on the button, the whole clock would resound like a distant Sunday morning church bell. He watched the arm swinging inside the glass case, back and forth and forth and back, in time with the rhythm of the room. His local was his sanctuary, a place that provided him with the necessary distractions and respite from the unforgiving emptiness of his flat.

Just before his wife had passed away, she'd made him promise he wouldn't grieve for her or dwell too long on things now lost, but it was difficult. He'd often wake in the night and feel the warmth of her body next to him, or hear the sound of her quiet breathing, like the gentle rhythm of the clock. He was the snorer, but she'd always slept like an angel, even at the height of her illness. There were times when he'd come home from the bookies, or the pub, and the flat would be filled with the smell of her Scotch broth or home-baked rice pudding, and he'd find himself in the kitchen, waiting for her to welcome him home. Now it was all tins and meals for one from Scotmid. He didn't mind that so much, but it was her company he missed, her ever-present laughter, and her cuddles at night to help him away. He visited her grave every week to renew the flowers and keep it all tidy, as she would have liked it, but it was little comfort. Seeing her name engraved on the cold granite plinth only served to remind him that she was gone for good.

Jean's great love was dancing, and she'd insist on a trip to the Palais every couple of weeks. And while James would often complain to her that he was too tired after a long week at work, her exuberant joy on the dance floor was infectious and impossible to resist. He was quite partial to lindy hop, as it got his heart going, but she adored the waltz. He'd moan and say he was no good at it, but secretly he loved it. The closeness of their bodies dancing together in time made him feel young again and free of the weight of age. He raised his glass and quietly toasted his absent wife. Downing his drink quickly, he was about to leave when a group of youngsters arrived, bringing some much-needed life and laughter in from the street.

'Hello, my friend,' one of the young men said when he spotted James at the bar.

'Hello, Andy. How are you?'

James had first met Andy back when he was a wide-eyed fresher at the university. Andy was a volunteer reader at the local cancer care hospice. Every Saturday morning he'd turn up armed with the latest thriller and read to James' wife, whose lymphoma had past the point of intervention. Andy had lost his own mum to cancer when he was 15, so volunteering was his way of giving back and saying thank you to the NHS for the care his mum had received. But his weekly bedside vigils became so much more to him. His blossoming friendship with Jean and James helped him release all the pain of losing his mum that had become blocked inside, and as the weeks and months passed, the weight he'd been carrying around seemed to slowly slip from his rounded shoulders. In return, Jean and James grew very fond of him, until eventually he became more like a surrogate grandson, sharing the happy – and difficult – times, as Jean's cancer slowly consumed her body and mind. Andy demonstrated an inner strength that reminded James of himself. When Jean was at her worst, Andy didn't run as others of his age might have. He carried on, week after week, reading another page or two of some dark, gruesome tale. Jean was particularly keen on violent serial killers, which always made Andy laugh. And even when she was almost completely out of it, doped up to the eyeballs on morphine, Andy ploughed on, recognising that James needed him there maybe more than Jean.

Since Jean's death, Andy and James had continued their friendship, and every few weeks Andy would make a point of catching up with James at his local. But, what with the final exams and everything else going on in Andy's life recently, he hadn't been around as much as he would have liked. So, as the world rattled at Andy's door, he thought it was high time he saw his old friend again. And because it was so close to James and Jean's wedding anniversary, he called on some friends to help him set up a wee surprise celebratory reunion. Despite some initial protestations from one or two, who were keen to get the end-of-an-era party started, they all rallied round. James had been part of their journey through uni too, and they didn't want to let him down.

Andy shook James's hand. 'I'm doing OK,' he said, smiling. 'We're all out on the town tonight. We've just finished our exams.'

'Is that your finals?' James asked.

'Aye, all done. It's in the lap of the gods now.'

'Well, that's splendid. And you'll be fine, you're a smart kid. I can't believe that's four years gone.

'I know, it's flown by.'

'You'll be married with six weans before you know it,' said James, grinning.

'Oh God, no,' said Andy. 'I need to see the world first.'

'Well, don't leave it too late.' James pulled on his coat.

'You're not going, are you?'

'Aye, it's getting late, and I have important business to attend to.'

'Oh aye, what's that then?'

'My bed.'

They both laughed.

'Who's the girl?' asked James, nodding towards the group.

'That's Lorna.'

'She's bonny.'

Andy smiled. 'She is.'

'A new click eh?' James nudged his friend gently.

'Maybe,' said Andy. 'A man can only try.'

'Indeed. And keep on trying.'

'She was on the same course as me, but our paths never really crossed till now.'

'So, something in common then, aside from the obvious.'

'Let me buy you a drink,' said Andy. 'Please. And come over and join us. They'd all love to see you.'

James wrestled with the buttons on his coat. 'No, you're alright. One's enough for me these days. I think I would be what you might call a geriatric gooseberry.'

'Not at all. You're one of the crew. The guys love your company.'

'Crew?' James grimaced. 'Maybe another night, eh?'

'No, I mean, we're all – ' Andy was on the verge of spilling the beans.

'It's mine and Jean's wedding anniversary tomorrow,' James cut in. 'So I need to get back.'

'Oh God, I'm sorry, James,' said Andy, 'I completely forgot. How many years were you married?'

'This would be our 50th.'

'Well, bugger that,' said Andy. 'We can't let you go home on your own now.'

'I'll be fine.' James waved across at the group in the corner. 'Have a good night!' he shouted.

'Oh, come on, Jim,' Andy pleaded. 'Just the one. It wouldn't be the same, us celebrating without you.'

James politely declined again, and with a final handshake was out the door and gone.

Andy turned to the barman, who was also in on the attempted sting. 'Oh well, we did try.'

'Aye, he's a stubborn bastard at the best of times.'

The landlord lined up the drinks. Andy emptied his wallet onto the counter and counted out a handful of notes. 'How much?' he asked, bracing himself for the answer. But before the landlord could respond, a soft hand touched Andy on the shoulder.

'I'll get these.' It was James.

'You're back.'

'Well, a wee voice said to me what good are you at home when you should be raising a glass to Andy and his friends' achievements.'

'That's brilliant,' said Andy. 'I was worried about you.'

'Well, now you don't have to be. And I don't want any argument from you about the round, okay?'

Andy nodded reluctantly. 'That's way too generous.'

'After all you've done for us?' said James. 'Away with ye.'

Andy carried the drinks over to the table and introduced James to those who didn't already know him. When it was Lorna's turn, she smiled and kissed James gently on the cheek.

'Look at him,' said Iain, one of Andy's friends. Iain had known James about as long as Andy, and had shared a few bets on the same no hope runners and riders.

'Lovely to meet you,' said Lorna.

'I think you're in there, Jimbo,' laughed Iain, trying to embarrass him.

'Give it up Iain,' said Andy. 'You're never going to get to Jim.'

'This is very true,' said Iain, raising his pint. 'Cheers James, and cheers everyone.' He noticed James wasn't drinking. 'Where's yours?'

James shook his head. 'I've had my quota for the evening.'

'Sorry pal, that's not allowed. You don't get off that easily.' And before James could stop him, Iain was up ordering him another whisky. When he got back, he resumed his toast.

'To the future!'

Andy stopped him. 'No,' he said. 'This one is to Jean and James. Happy anniversary!'

Everyone roared, and James raised his glass with a reluctant smile.

∾

Over the course of the next two hours, James listened and smiled as the university friends recalled their exploits from the previous four years. It all sounded so exhausting to him. The youngsters were careful to include him in their conversation, and once in a while one or another of them would ask what he got up to in his youth. James remained politely discreet about his past. Not on account of anything shameful, but because he genuinely believed he'd led a pretty unremarkable life. Anything he could add to the conversation would most likely bore them to tears.

'You're very slow with that whisky,' said Iain.

'Leave him,' interrupted Lorna. 'The man is happy as he is. We're not all drunken idiots like you.' She slid her chair closer to James. 'It's lovely to finally meet you,' she said, leaning in towards him. 'Andy thinks very highly of you. Says you're younger than all of us.'

'I am,' said James, deadpan, 'and it costs me a great deal of money to pay him to say these things.'

Lorna smiled and sipped her beer, before leaning in closer. 'Andy told me about your wife. I'm so sorry.'

James shrugged.

'Sorry, I didn't mean to – '

'That's alright,' said James, smiling. 'I don't mind talking about her. She likes it too.'

Lorna narrowed her eyes at him for a moment, a little unsure. 'What was she like?'

James rubbed the back of his neck. 'She was bright, way beyond me. And funny with it. She'd say it as she saw it, without all the usual embroidery. But she could do it without offending anyone. She just made them laugh. She'd get away with murder.' He paused to take another nip of whisky. 'When she got ill, she found ways to help everyone around her cope. That's how she was.'

'It must've been devastating.'

'I don't miss her,' James said abruptly. 'She won't let me.'

'What?' Lorna was thrown by his response.

'She's in here.' James tapped the side of his head with his forefinger. 'And every day she reminds me to live right here, in the now.'

'That's a very positive way of dealing with it.'

'She wouldn't have it any other way. She doesn't give me a choice.'

'Well, here's to you, Jean, and here's to *the now*.' Lorna raised her glass.

After the toast, they sat in silence for a moment, listening to the various conversations criss-crossing the table. 'He's a good man,' said James.

'Who?' Lorna asked, feigning confusion.

'You know who.' James smiled.

'Oh, he's a big eejit.' Lorna laughed, causing Andy to look over, puzzled.

'Sometimes the eejit is the one.'

Iain butted into the conversation, just in time.

'James, James, put that girl down and answer this question. Who sang "San Francisco"? You know…' And he broke into a toneless rendition of the chorus.

'Tony Bennett,' said James automatically.

'I told you, Stevie,' said Iain to his friend, who shook his head in dismay. Iain turned back to James. 'He thought it was Paul Anka, whoever the hell that is.'

'He wrote "My Way".'

'I always thought that was Sinatra,' said Iain.

Lorna butted in. 'Sinatra never wrote a word. Bennett is the king of swing.'

'You like swing?' James asked her, surprised.

'I *am* swing,' said Lorna, standing up and wiggling her hips seductively.

'… or a swinger,' Iain joked, and everyone laughed.

∾

Later, Andy caught James on his way back from the loo. 'Listen, we're all heading into town for something to eat. Come with us. It'll be fun.'

James snuck a furtive look over at the grandfather clock in the corner. 'No, no, it's way past my bedtime.'

'Come on. We're going to a Malaysian restaurant. You ever tried Malaysian?'

James patted Andy on the chest. 'You may be surprised to hear that I've had plenty of Malaysian cuisine. I did part of my National Service there. Back then it was called Malay.'

'You dark horse,' said Iain, sidling up. 'I bet you've got a few tales to tell about that.'

'Well, there you go,' said Andy. 'It's fate. It's supposed to be very authentic, isn't that right, Stevie?'

Stevie stood up from the table. 'If it's shite you can all blame me.'

'Look, I tell you what,' said Andy, 'we'll take you there, and then sort you out with a taxi after. How does that sound?'

James swithered. 'Well … seeing as it's been over 50 years …'

Jackets and coats and wallets and handbags were quickly grabbed. James followed them out, shaking his head at the unexpected way his night was panning out.

'Be good,' The landlord shouted after them, winking at James as they left.

'It's good to be out,' James said to Lorna as they waited at the rank for a taxi. It had been a long while since he'd ventured further than the pub. And aside from a trip to his solicitors to sort out a problem with the flat, he hadn't been into town for over two years. After Jean died, his old friends had hung around for a while, inviting him to dinners and summer barbecues – even Christmas drinks

– but slowly the invites dwindled, then stopped completely. Jean's absence had left an almost physical hole, too painful for her friends to deal with. It didn't help that James was monosyllabic and unreachable for most of that first period of mourning. Jean was missing from the group, and the rhythm of their friendship had been altered beyond repair. James' son too had all but disappeared off the face of the earth. He'd only seen Davie a couple of times in the past year, and it had always ended in some argument or another. James wasn't sure why, but Davie had been angry with him for years now.

The group bundled into two taxis, James sharing with Andy and Lorna. He found himself between them, but quickly made an excuse to sit by the window, spreading himself out in the seat so that Andy had to squeeze in closer to Lorna. Along the way, he wondered if he'd made a mistake and should have gone home when he'd had the chance. He was tired, and the two whiskies were swimming around his head like sharks. 'Oh, what the hell,' he thought. 'Jean would have been the first in the cab.'

∽

The restaurant was tucked away in an alley between Byres Road and the university. It was packed with students, with a smattering of couples and end-of-term boozers. The group pushed their way through the queue as Stevie confirmed their booking with a waiter in full Malaysian costume. He took them to a table at the rear of the dining room. James let Lorna get seated first, and she, in turn, invited him to sit next to her. He waited until Andy was sitting opposite her before handing his coat to the waiter. A second waiter in colourful headgear approached the table and took their drinks orders. Despite loud protestations from Iain, James refused another whisky, although he eventually relented and accepted a pint.

The noise in the restaurant was deafening and James struggled to hear much of what was said. Yet, despite his awkwardness at being the only pensioner in the room, he found himself enjoying the experience, and revelling in the nostalgic sights, sounds, and smells of long forgotten times.

'Do you like it?' Lorna asked, leaning in so he could hear her.

'Aye, it takes me back.'

'How long were you there?'

'About two years.'

'Did you know your wife then?'

'I met her there,' said James. 'She was an army nurse. I asked her out and she turned me down.'

'Why?'

'She told me I was an eejit.'

Lorna laughed. 'So have you got some tales to tell, then?' she asked, nudging his arm.

'That's for me to know.' If he were younger, he would say she was flirting with him, and he liked it.

He picked up the menu but couldn't read it without his glasses, so he ordered some satay, the only thing he could vaguely remember from his time there. When the food arrived, he was horrified to see the amount being delivered to the table. He quietly nibbled on a few sticks of fried chicken as the others gorged on mountainous platefuls of curry and rice, and a vast array of other strange and sizzling culinary delights. He remembered when his own appetite was as urgent and relentlessly unfulfilled as theirs, and a part of him longed for that feeling again. As the meal progressed, and more and more food and alcohol were consumed, James found it increasingly difficult to maintain his concentration. He hadn't drunk this much in years, but it felt good to be light-headed, and among the young and the living for a change. His mind began to wander back to his National Service days and his first encounter with Jean.

'As it's our anniversary,' he muttered under his breath and tapped his head again.

She was such a stunner, especially in her uniform. All his friends told him he was punching above his weight, but he persisted. He must have asked her out at least ten times before she finally relented. But their first date was a disaster. He took her to a bar that turned out to be a strip club, and this seemed to confirm her worst fears about him. She called it off and refused to return his calls or letters. And then he heard she'd been posted back to Scotland. But he never gave up, and when he found out which hospital she was working in he wrote to the ward every day for five months. Finally, she called him. He could still remember running to the phone booth and almost snapping the cord when he picked up the receiver. When he heard her voice, he knew he would never let her go again.

'Are you OK?' asked Lorna.

'Aye,' said James, slowly returning to the present.

'How's the food?'

'A bit spicier than I remember, but so are most things these days.'

Lorna grinned. 'So how did you win Jean round, after she turned you down?'

'Blackmail.'

Lorna pulled a face and laughed.

∾

After another round of drinks, the bill was paid. This time, Andy refused to let James contribute. Out on the street, the cold of the night hit James' system and his head spun. He stumbled forward, Lorna only just managing to catch his arm.

'I'm a wee bit off the pace,' he said. Rubbing his eyes, he thanked them all for their hospitality and said he should probably go home now.

'We'll walk you to the taxi rank,' said Andy. But instead of heading down onto Byres Road, they took a right up the lane towards the university.

'Where are we going?' asked James.

'I know a quieter rank,' said Andy.

They wobbled and weaved their drunken way through the uni buildings, and as they approached the Union, James thought he could hear the sound of trumpets pumping out a familiar melody.

'Is that "Mack the Knife"?' he asked Lorna.

'You could be right,' she said, glancing across at Andy.

When they reached the entrance, they stopped.

'Looks like it's swing night,' said Andy.

A couple dressed in 1950s-style outfits squeezed past them and through the door of the Union.

'And fancy dress too, by the looks of things. What do you say we have a wee look?'

James was about to say no, but the booze had lowered his levels of resistance and the music was way too seductive. Lorna took his arm again and led him slowly up the steps.

'Is he a member?' the porter asked briskly, pointing at James.

Andy leaned over the counter and muttered something to the man under his breath. Then he stood back. 'So I can sign him in then?' he asked.

'Aye,' said the porter with a smile, 'but you better behave yourself in there.'

They followed a group of girls in polka dot dresses and colourful cardigans along a corridor into a large, noisy auditorium, packed with students in similar period clothes. A big band was in full swing, blasting out a lively version of "Rags to Riches".

'Now *that's* Bennett!' Lorna shouted over the din and swung her hips. James looked around the hall. It was decorated with retro posters and 1950s' memorabilia, a large mirror ball on the ceiling scattering tiny crystals of dazzling white light across the room. The dance floor was rammed full of people spinning and turning in time with the *thump, thump, thump* of the horns. Maybe it was the alcohol rush from the walk up the hill, or the familiarity of the music, but James suddenly felt fifty years younger. He had an overwhelming desire to join the young revellers on the dance floor.

Iain mumbled something to Andy and disappeared into the crowd. The rest of the group filtered off in different directions. James followed Lorna and Andy to a table on the edge of the dance floor.

'Drink?' Andy mouthed to James.

'No more for me,' said James, his eyes still fixed on the dancing.

They sat down, James careful not to get between the two lovebirds again.

'What do you think?' Andy shouted over the band.

James nodded enthusiastically. 'A pretty good effort.'

Lorna pushed her chair back. 'Okay, who's up for a dance?'

James and Andy shook their heads.

'Oh, come on,' protested Lorna. 'Listen to those fabulous horns. How can you resist?'

James rubbed the top of his leg. 'I'm no sure my hip is up to it.'

'Well, there's only one way to find out.' Lorna stood up and held out her hand. 'Come on, James,' she said. 'Show me how it's done.' James glanced across the table at Andy, already clapping his approval.

'Go on,' said Andy, 'you know you want to.'

James looked up at Lorna again, and for a fleeting moment, under the sparkle of the mirror ball, she looked just like Jean in her heyday. The band broke into "What A Wonderful World".

'Come on,' Lorna said again. 'You can't turn down Satchmo.'

James forced himself up from the table and let himself be led onto the dance floor. The mismatched couple took up a relaxed waltz position and began shuffling gently together from side to side. Staring at his feet, James moved one awkwardly, and then the other, just as awkwardly, if not more so. It wasn't long before he stepped on Lorna's toes.

'I seem to be a bit rusty,' he said. Lorna smiled and encouraged him to move in time with her. As they danced, he moved a little closer, his feet slowly remembering. As the song continued, James' technique returned and the pain in his hip seemed to diminish. He closed his eyes and suddenly he was back in the Palais, in Jean's arms. He drew Lorna in closer, their moves now fluent and smooth. He attempted a spin, and Lorna followed intuitively.

'You're not too bad at all,' she said, smiling.

Lorna's voice brought James back to the present. He opened his eyes and stopped.

'What's the matter?' asked Lorna.

James looked over at the table. Andy smiled back, giving them both the thumbs up. James gestured for him to come over. Andy shook his head, but James persisted. Finally, the reluctant dancer got up and joined them.

'Your turn,' said James.

'I can't follow that,' said Andy, shaking his head. 'You two were brilliant.'

Giving him no choice, James stepped out from between them and returned to the table.

The music stopped for a moment and, from the comfort of his seat, James watched the young couple shuffle around awkwardly. But then the band launched into "It Had To Be You" and Lorna took Andy's hand in hers and they began to dance gently together. As the song progressed, they moved closer and closer, Andy's arm creeping around the small of Lorna's back. When the song ended, they stood for a moment as though transfixed by what had just occurred. And then they kissed.

James smiled. 'About bloody time,' he said under his breath.

Andy and Lorna returned to the table hand in hand. Lorna asked if James would like a drink, but he politely declined. Smiling, she placed a hand on his shoulder. 'Will you be okay for a minute?' she asked.

'Don't you worry about me,' said James. 'I'm having a ball.'

Lorna headed off to the bar with Andy, his arm draped over her shoulder. James continued to watch the dancing and soon lost himself in the music. From time to time, he'd glance back at the bar. He could see the two of them standing together, Andy leaning on the counter, trying to look handsome. James smiled, remembering how hard he used to have to work to maintain the illusion of coolness himself. But then the smile dropped. The conversation at the bar now seemed to take a serious turn, and Andy appeared agitated. He dropped Lorna's hand and walked off. She waited at the bar a moment or two, but when Andy didn't come back, she returned to the table.

'Where's your man?' asked James.

'I don't know. I think he went to the loo.' She seemed rattled. James thought she might burst into tears.

'What's happened?' he asked.

'I think I upset him. I should have been straight about it.'

'About what?'

'I've landed a job.'

'Well, that's fantastic,' said James, although he sensed a 'but' approaching.

'It's in Berlin. I leave in a couple of weeks.'

'So, I take it Andy wasn't pleased.'

'He just went off. He didn't even bother to congratulate me.'

'Let me go see if I can find him.'

'No, don't do that.'

'I'll be back in a minute.'

'Sorry,' said Lorna, forcing a smile. 'I didn't mean to spoil your night.'

'It's not over yet,' said James. As he pulled himself up, his hip spasmed, sending a sudden surge of pain down his leg. He turned away so Lorna wouldn't see him wince. Following the signs to the loos, James hobbled out of the auditorium. The sudden silence in the corridor roared in his ears like a jet engine.

Andy was at the sink washing his hands. James entered, nodded to him, and limped over to the urinal.

'Great night, Andy.'

'It's always great to hang out with you, James.'

'Looks like you've landed a good one there.'

'I thought I had.'

'It's never about the thinking, Andy.' James finished up and joined his friend at the sink. 'Lorna told me about her new job.'

'Why didn't she say anything before I made a complete arse of myself?' asked Andy, addressing the question more to his reflection in the mirror than to anyone else.

'She's told you now.'

'But it's too bloody late. *I'm* too bloody late.'

James stopped washing his hands and turned around.

'Listen, Andy. You know when I first met Jean, she wasn't in the least bit interested. She thought I was a loser, and in some ways I was. But I just kept on and on at her. I wrote to her and sent her flowers and phoned her and wrote again. But still she wouldn't have it. And then she moved away, down to Bristol. It took me over a month to find out where she was, and then I followed her down. She must've thought I was bloody stalking her. I visited her every day at her work, with more flowers and more words. And for some reason, she took pity on me and gave me a second chance.'

'But she's going to Berlin, not Bristol.'

'I would have gone anywhere. I just knew that if I didn't keep trying I would regret it for the rest of my life.'

'But what if it doesn't work out?'

'So what! It could be happy ever after or a total disaster. Who knows? She might break your heart or you might break hers, but she could be the one. If you don't go, you'll never know.'

Andy dried his hands, saying nothing. But as they left, James stopped him in the doorway and took his arm.

'Go son, go with her. Don't hesitate for a second.'

They returned to the auditorium just as the band broke into a full-bodied version of "Witchcraft", this time with a crooner giving it his all.

Lorna wasn't at the table. They both scanned the room, before James spotted her dancing with Iain. He had his arm wrapped tightly round her waist as though he was trying to squeeze the life out of her; as though she were captured prey.

'Looks like somebody needs saving.' The words were barely out of James' mouth before Andy was marching past him, his body aimed at the dancing couple.

James eased himself back down onto his chair. His hip continued to spasm, and he knew he'd have to go home soon. When Andy reached the dance floor, there was a brief exchange of words between him and Iain, resulting in the latter's ungracious retreat. Andy then took Lorna in his arms and they danced together in silence. When the song ended, they carried on dancing until they finally stopped and embraced. Another song began, but they continued to kiss, forcing other couples to manoeuvre around them. At last they came up for air, before disappearing into the crowd. A few moments later, they re-emerged at the table.

'We're going together,' Andy said, his arm still wrapped around Lorna's waist.

'You mean you're taking this eejit with you?' James said to Lorna.

'It looks that way.'

'Well, I wish you both all the happiness in the world.'

'Let's start with Berlin,' Lorna said with a smile.

'Now I think it's time I was away home,' said James. 'You've kept me out long enough, you rambling buggers.'

Out at reception, Andy helped James on with his coat.

'Can't take the pace, eh?' the porter said.

'I showed them a thing or two,' James replied with a wink.

The unsteady threesome made their way down to the taxi rank. As they approached the small queue, James stopped.

'You planned all of this, didn't you?' he said to Andy.

'What?' Andy said, feigning surprise, and then burst out laughing. 'We wanted to say farewell properly, and it wasn't a night for you to go home on your own.'

'But how did you know about my National Service in Malaysia?' asked James.

Andy dug his hands into his pockets. 'I never told you this before, but when I was reading to Jean and you'd leave us for a while to go for a cup of tea, she'd order me to put my book down. She'd tell me all these stories from her life: growing up in Dennistoun, the nurses' college she went to and the young doctors she met there.' Andy raised his eyebrows at James, who threw him a disapproving look. 'And then on to her adventures in Malaysia and Hong Kong. But most of the time she'd talk about you and what a special person you were. Her life was amazing and a million miles better than the trash I was reading her. She swore me to secrecy because she knew how embarrassed you'd be.'

'She's right about that,' said James.

'And yes, of course I knew it was your anniversary,' Andy continued. 'She told me all about your disastrous wedding reception.'

'Her gate-crashing mad aunty. It took three relatives and the minister to restrain her.' James laughed. 'I feel well and truly duped.'

Lorna reached over and touched James on the arm. 'Andy knew if we'd asked you, you'd have just said no.'

'Sorry, James. But it's so tough saying goodbye, you know?'

∾

The bouncer on the line let James jump the queue, surprised to see someone his age out so late and in the thick of it all.

'We'll see you again before we go,' said Lorna. James knew that was unlikely, but it was a gentler way to say goodbye.

'Thanks for tonight,' said James. 'You made an old man feel even older.'

Andy smiled. 'No, thank you.' He took James' hand and shook it briskly. Lorna gave James a hug and a peck on the cheek. 'You're a lovely man,' she said into his ear, and gently tapped the side of his head with her finger.

'What was that?' Andy asked.

'That's for us to know,' smiled Lorna.

James waved his final goodbyes, and with Andy's help, he slowly climbed into the taxi. As it pulled away, he turned back and watched the young lovers embrace and then disappear into the night.

∞

Back home, James made his weary way up the three flights to his flat, stopping on every landing to catch his breath and relieve the pain now shooting down both his legs. He let himself in on the second attempt, his fingers – or was it the key? – not wanting to play. Hanging up his coat he went straight to the bedroom. But as began removing his clothes, he changed his mind. 'This was a special night,' he thought, and turned around.

In the kitchen, James searched the cupboards until he found a small bottle of brandy, tucked away behind a pile of dinner plates. From the side cabinet, he removed two crystal glasses, Jean's favourite wedding present. He poured out two small halves and carried them into the living room. He took an old shoebox full of photographs from the sideboard and emptied the contents onto the dining table, spreading out the images. He was looking for one in particular that he loved.

And then he spotted it. He picked it out and held it up to the light. It was a black and white shot of them together, standing outside the Palais, all dressed up and ready to dance. He could remember her dress, her hair, and the scent of her perfume on the nape of her neck. She was radiant and beautiful, and her vitality seemed to illuminate everything around her, including the young James. Returning to the sideboard, he plugged in an old portable record player sitting on top. He fumbled through a small pile of vinyl records on the floor, until he found the one he was looking for. Placing the needle gently on the disk, he turned up the volume. The old LP crackled and hissed, but then the song began, and the soar of the strings drowned out all the blemishes of age. It was Jean's favourite and he hadn't played it since she died. But tonight she had allowed him to return to their time, and "Embraceable You" seemed to be the only song to play.

James stood in the middle of the room. Ignoring the pain from his hip, he swayed lightly from side to side in time with the music and Ella Fitzgerald's dark velvet voice. He closed his eyes and let the swoon of the strings take him to her. When she saw him approaching, she smiled, her radiance filling his limbs with energy and youthful light. He wrapped his arm around her waist and drew her to him. He could feel the warmth of her skin beneath the thin fabric of her summer dress. Her hand slipped inside his. It was soft and cool, just as he remembered it. And as they gently waltzed, he leaned in and kissed the nape of her neck, pulling her closer still until they folded into each other and became one.

The song ended and he held her for a moment longer, afraid to let go. She touched his cheek and smiled, and then she slowly disappeared into the darkness of the room. James sat down and looked again at the photograph. 'Happy anniversary, my darling. I love you,' he whispered, and toasted his wife. The brandy finished, he turned off the lights and made his weary way to bed. As he lay in the darkness with the trumpets still roaring in his ears, he found himself muttering under his breath, *the now, the now, the now,* until the waves rolled in and over him and he was at last asleep.

Acknowledgements

We would like to thank the following people for their tireless guidance, support, wisdom, encouragement, patience, and life-saving humour on our long road to completing this project: our editor and oracle maker, Jo Haywood; our publisher and commander in chief, Jamie McGarry; demon barber and cut throat razor expert, Gordon Robertson; artist Lucy Hawkins for her cinemascopically beautiful cover art; and all the team at Valley Press.

Peace, love and poetry

All best

Tom, John, Paul

Paul Cowan's 'Vinegar Stroke' previously appeared in *Untitled*; 'Wise Old Owl' in *The Ogilvie*; 'Rab The Stab' in the anthology *Alight Here*; and 'On A Bench' in *Octavius*. Tom Gillespie's 'Craw' previously appeared in *Untitled*, and 'Where Was I?' in *The Ogilvie*.